Compensation and Accountability

With acknowledgements to Dr Kate Allsopp who
produced the Conference and to Miss Mary-Lou Nesbitt
who produced this book.

Compensation and Accountability

Keeping the Balance

Proceedings of a Medical Defence Union Conference
held on 13 May 1991

Edited by Dr John Wall

MERCURY

First published in 1992
by Mercury Books
Gold Arrow Publications Limited
862 Garratt Lane, London SW17 ONB

Set in Palatino by TecSet Ltd. Wallington, Surrey
Printed and bound in Great Britain by
Mackays of Chatham, PLC, Chatham, Kent

British Library Cataloguing in Publication Data is available

ISBN 1–85251–175–3

Contents

Dr Robert Maxwell

Chairman's introduction

Dr Robert Maxwell
Secretary, The King's Fund

Good morning, everyone. Nice to see you all here. The twin issues for discussion, as you know, are accountability in the sense of both personal and collective accountability to the public and also compensation, but the day is designed so that we do try to keep those things which are so entwined slightly distinct in our minds. We will start with accountability this morning. I think we're trying to see a way forward, particularly with the help of our overseas visitors and benefit from their experience. I am certain in my own mind that whatever happens in this country – the present situation is not stable – we're not likely to stay where we are. We have the chance today to think about where we might get to on the basis of what's happened so far and whether we like that and whether we can change it in any way. Those of you who are here actually do have, in one way or another, quite a substantial amount of influence and power to move the agenda in a particular direction if, together, we can be clear what that direction might be.

I'd like to introduce the speakers to you and we begin with Sir George Pinker.

1

Sir George Pinker

Accountability: is there a better system?

Sir George Pinker

Immediate Past President of The Royal College of Obstetricians and Gynaecologists

Good morning Mr Chairman, Ladies and Gentlemen. It's an honour to be here and to take part in the proceedings of today's relatively unique meeting and one which perhaps should have been in the field some long time ago to guide us in our deliberations over the forthcoming problems. I feel I'm really here under false pretences because I'm not an expert in these matters but of course it has affected our specialty more than any other specialty in medicine. And as I was, in a sense, slightly dragooned into doing this, I'm here without informed consent.

The conference is organised by the Medical Defence Union (MDU) against the background of the surge of increase in litigation over the past five or six years. Between 1983 and 1989 it increased by a factor of three or more. And I'm told reliably that if you add up the various defence organisations' files there's always one new brain-damaged child on the table each day of the year, something like 360. And of course with the enormous sums that are being awarded it is a very serious matter both fiscally, for the profession and in terms of practice. I finished as President of the Royal College of Obstetricians & Gynaecologists (RCOG) last October and I've had personal experience of the effect that this had on our specialty. It has affected recruitment. It's affected the staying power of the juniors and we've had a fall-off rate in our juniors, even after they have obtained membership of the RCOG, of up to 20 per cent per year for the last three years, which is really quite a serious figure.

Underlining today's discussions is the background problem of litigation and its effect on clinical practice in this country. But it's really not that matter which we're here to debate. It will be fairly clear from the format of the meeting that the MDU believes that compensation can be separated from accountability and that this general approach has much to offer the British public and the British healthcare professions. Much ill-informed debate is based on misinformation or misunderstanding about the system of accountability and compensation and these have been tried in overseas countries and we're very fortunate to have with us the speakers we have here today to tell us something of their experience.

Seen from the point of view of an obstetrician, litigation is certainly not the right way to hold the clinician accountable to the individual patient or to the community. It takes an average of nearly five years to process a case. Gross errors result in settlements out-of-court anyway, so that in the field of litigation the patient will probably never attend a meeting at which he hears the other side of the story and trials of civil claims are rare birds. Dr Wall of the MDU tells me that at a recent debate in the Hunterian Society on the thesis *Litigation is bad for your health* (which was incidentally carried by 54 votes to 17) Sir Cecil Clothier, who was formerly the NHS Ombudsman and is now Chairman of the Council on Tribunals, argued that litigation provided the necessary catharsis when things had gone wrong between doctor and patient.

In Britain we have the General Medical Council (GMC) to consider allegations of serious medical and professional misconduct. It is often said that if it were not possible to litigate then the GMC ought to take within its remit a greatly increased number of problems. Mr Nigel Spearing MP has on a number of occasions proposed a Private Member's Bill requiring the GMC to deal with matters of conduct not amounting to serious professional misconduct[1]. The GMC at least holds doctors accountable throughout the country whether within the NHS or not. The NHS Ombudsman deals with administrative matters mainly.

The proposal, a few years ago, that the NHS Ombudsman should deal with clinical matters was dropped when stage three of the complaints procedure or Independent Professional Review[2], as it is known, was introduced, in which two consultants (assessors from the same specialty or specialties) and one from a different region, interview the patient who has a sense of grievance about the outcome of hospital treatment. And this has worked really very well but it's a slow, laborious process which takes months and the paperwork is heavy, and it's a cumbersome procedure but it does work well when it gets into gear. It's very obvious from the results that come back that one of the chief problems is communication between the patient and the doctors involved. Often the first time they've ever met or discussed the matter openly is at the third stage of the complaints procedure, something which should have happened right at the beginning and would have obviated the need for all this performance.

With audit and peer review there are thus a number of systems of professional accountability already in existence. I think the purpose of today's meeting is to hear whether there is a better system which those representing the British patient and consumer, the healthcare professions and the government, present or future, could helpfully take into their calculations in the debate in Britain. And I shall listen as avidly as you will to those who are going to advise us this morning. Thank you.

References

1. Amendment Bill to Section 36 of the Medical Act 1983.
2. HC(81)5.

Mr Christopher James

Professional accountability in New Zealand 1974–1991: doctor, patient and advocate

Mr Christopher James
Solicitor, Wellington, New Zealand

'Ka tangi te titi
Ka tangi tc kaka
Kai tangi hoki ko au
Te hei mauroria'

That's nothing to do with Andrew Lloyd Webber. It's a Maori prayer of the Ngati Porou tribe. This appropriately leads me into my topic: accident compensation lives on in New Zealand and doctors still maintain reasonable standards despite their virtual immunity from damages claims. 'Hark the bird sings, the parrot cries and I cry Behold there is life.' The scheme and its philosophy is in good heart in New Zealand, though it is subject to review at present and about to weather winds of change as my learned compatriot, Sir Kenneth Keith, may outline for you.

Dr Maxwell, distinguished guests, I am indeed honoured to be here before you today in these revered surroundings. In the batting order I seem to be elevated to that rather uncomfortable position of opening bat or more accurately, following Sir George, first drop. In this illustrious line-up we

7

have today I would be first to recognise my luck making night watchman.

My brief is to consider, with reference to that rather incompatible trio of bedfellows, the doctor, the patient and the advocate, the development and operation of professional accountability over the past 17 years or so that the New Zealand 'no-fault' scheme has been in existence. I've been asked to share with you my experience gained over 21 years as an adviser to the MDU and its members in New Zealand.

Briefly, to put you in the picture. New Zealand is inhabited by, at the last count, 60 million sheep, 3.2 million humans and 6,500 doctors, which gives a ratio of 60 to 3.2 to .0065.

The first question to consider is how did the 1974 demise of the medical malpractice damages cases in New Zealand affect this trio in my country? I'll deal with the latter first: the advocate.

Accident compensation was to the specialist personal injury lawyers in New Zealand what the 1830 potato blight was to the spud farmer in Ireland. It damn near wiped them out. But lest you should feel any sympathy for that rather endangered species I hasten to point out that because of their rather inherent craft, skill, initiative and resilience, those lawyers found fresh and rewarding fields and avenues of the law awaiting their creation. Some sought spiritual guidance and on occasion those lawyers could be found crouched in a rather unaccustomed position at the foot of their beds praying thus 'Stir up much strife amongst thy people, Lord, lest this, thy servant perish.'. And that plea for those lawyers was answered not so much by Divine Intervention but by the very nature of society itself. Some of them, of course, fled to the unblighted and greener pastures of Australia. As a result of which, some say, the IQ level of Australia palpably raised.

That disposes of the advocate. I move on now to the more important question – the patient and the doctor. What has happened now in this purified air devoid of writs and all those threatening pollutants associated with common law fallout? Do doctors run amok? Have standards fallen? What is the framework to regulate, monitor and punish them if they err? What remedy does the patient have who is wronged or injured by the errant doctor? And how effective is it?

The first remedy, in a sense, is the avenue of compensation itself pursuant to the rights conferred by the accident compensation legislation. Suffice it for me to only touch on this because I understand Sir Kenneth Keith will be detailing this. But I need to give you a framework. Our accident compensation legislation (Accident Compensation Act 1972) came into force in 1974. The Act was stipulated as being a code providing, and I quote:

'Where any person suffers personal injury by accident in New Zealand or dies as a result of personal injury so suffered, or where any person suffers outside New Zealand personal injury by accident in respect of which he has cover under this Act or dies as a result of personal injury so suffered, no proceedings for damages arising directly or indirectly out of the injury or death shall be brought in any court in New Zealand independently of this Act whether by that person or any other person and whether under any rule of law or any enactment.'

Thus the Accident Compensation Corporation (ACC) was vested with exclusive jurisdiction to determine whether or not any person suffered personal injury by accident.

The term 'personal injury' is the key and it is defined as including a range of harms, one of those being medical, surgical, dental or first aid misadventure. 'Medical misadventure' is not defined and over the years it has become wider in its interpretation as a result of case law. Initially it was interpreted very narrowly and restrictively. But this narrow interpretation was tested by review and appeal and was finally expanded. The courts held that the word 'misadventure' must be given its natural meaning which was summed up as bad fortune, mishap, something that's turned out badly for that particular victim. This concept of medical misadventure covered a much wider spectrum of personal injury than instances of medical negligence. Most, if not all, cases of medical negligence have components of medical misadventure, but not all medical misadventures would satisfy the requirements of successful actions of negligence, such as foreseeability, breach of duty, causation

9

and the like. The development of the concept is illustrated in a recent Court of Appeal judgement in the case of *Green v Matheson*[1] where the Court considered claims brought by women whose cervical cancer had been mismanaged at the National Women's Hospital, a leading obstetric hospital. Their Honours' approach in this case heralded a very wide, all-embracing interpretation. Suffice it for me to quote several passages from that judgement which will give an idea of its ambit.

'The plaintiff's claim is in respect of medical misadventure. These words are entirely apt to describe from the plaintiff's point of view everything culpable on the part of the defendants that she alleges to have occurred. The description applies whether the course of action be trespass to the person, breach of fiduciary duty or negligence and whether the failure alleged be insufficient or wrong treatment, failure to inform, misdiagnosis, misrepresentation or administrative shortcoming. It all arose from the way in which she was dealt with as a medical case. If a case was mishandled it was her misfortune or ill-luck. This falls squarely within the idea of misadventure.'

I should add as an aside, that even though the accident compensation legislation took away the right to claim for damages there is still left a limited civil field of exemplary or punitive damages. The rationale, I suspect, for retaining that vestige of the common law is that awards of such damages arise independently of the injury suffered. The object of exemplary or punitive damages is to punish the wrongdoer for high-handed, contemptuous conduct. To date there's been no such successful case against a doctor in New Zealand.

In addition to that medical misadventure definition I've taken from the Court of Appeal judgement, it has been held that medical misadventure also includes the consequences or complications following medical treatment, as long as those complications are rare, unusual or unlikely and are beyond the normal range of what is expected as a consequential failure of medical treatment, because certainty cannot be underwritten. Not all medical treatment is successful, only those that are rare or undesigned.

Having foreshadowed this background, the question can now be posed: do medical misadventure findings by the ACC in any way regulate the doctor? Do they in any way regulate the standards of medical practice? Does the prospect of such constitute a deterrent to keep that doctor on the straight and narrow? The answer is, to my mind, an emphatic no. It does not. It has little effect as there's no impact on the doctor in economic terms, or on his professional repute or in terms of punishment. In a sense it has little or no effect on the regulation monitoring side. There's no publicity of any consequence in the findings and my experience is that the medical profession fear little from the bureaucratic application of medical misadventure compensation payments. Thus there is little, if any, accountability in that system.

Does the removal of this threat of being sued for damages mean that the doctor can act with immunity and impunity, freed from the shackles of litigious lawyers and the need for defensive medicine? No longer the Damocles sword hanging precariously above them? Far from it. Enter centre stage, the Medical Practitioners' Disciplinary Committee (MPDC). This was set up in its present form by the Medical Practitioners Act 1968, some years before the advent of accident compensation. It was implemented to regulate in the main the behaviour of medical practitioners. Dr Brian Rhodes (then of the MDU secretariat) was in New Zealand and he made a very prophetic remark when the accident compensation legislation was being introduced. I recall him saying: 'This Medical Practitioners' Disciplinary Committee is certainly going to be busy now that the patient has been denied his or her day in court'. How true that has become. Table 1 on page 14 illustrates the trend over the years 1970–1990.

Some of you may know this extract from your famous diarist, Samuel Pepys, written some 300 years ago. It is as relevant today, I suggest, as it was years ago: 'This day the Duke of Gloucester died as a result of smallpox due to the great negligence of his doctors.' It illustrates most clearly and eloquently one of the in-built genetic failings of mankind that when treatment is not successful and complications ensue it is assumed that it must be someone's fault. This, of course, translates into 'It was the doctor's fault, I will complain'. But with the advent of no-fault legislation,

11

where do patients turn and how do they make these claims? Increasingly to the disciplinary tribunal.

The MPDC hearing is run like a commission of inquiry. It has become the main arbiter, judge and keeper of medical standards. Under the Medical Practitioners Act 1968 there are three tiers – three levels. Before I discuss how doctors and patients react to this I need just to outline a little of the structure of the MPDC and its function.

At the lowest level is the Divisional Disciplinary Committee which is based in the main regions of the country. It deals with the least serious of complaints – conduct unbecoming. It has limited powers and can really only censure a doctor.

The next level is the MPDC itself, and this is by far the most active of the regulatory bodies in the disciplinary field. It considers charges of professional misconduct and penalties at this level range from censure, a fine of up to $NZ1,000 (£300), conditions imposed on practice for up to three years; publication of details of the doctor's name and also the power to award costs against the doctor if the case goes against him. And that ranges from $NZ6,000 – $NZ36,000 (£2,000 – £12,000) depending on the length of the case. The aims of the MPDC are twofold. First, to resolve complaints justly and without undue delay, and second, and importantly, to foster better standards of medical practice in postgraduate education.

To enumerate the functions of the MPDC:

1. Providing and promoting an efficient mechanism for handling complaints about doctors.
2. Promoting good communication and a constructive two-way relationship between the community and the medical profession.
3. Promoting conciliation procedures for resolution of minor complaints.
4. Encouraging a better standard of practice where applicable and as an integral part of the disciplinary process requiring doctors to undertake appropriate courses of re-training and education and be subject to peer revision.

Quite a wide spread, I would suggest.

The third level of seriousness of offence is disgraceful conduct in a professional respect, and this is dealt with by the Medical Council (the Council). The Council is not only the registration body, but it also considers appeals from the level below (the MPDC). Cases involving a doctor's conviction of criminal offences go direct to the Council. It is the only body, at present, which can strike a practitioner off the register. It can also suspend a doctor for up to 12 months.

These tribunals are made up of doctors with lay representation and each tribunal is assisted by a legal assessor who is a senior barrister and, on occasions, a retired High Court judge.

What about the cost of all this, you might ask? It's interesting to note that the cost of this disciplinary activity is met by the profession itself in the form of levies upon practitioners. It has resisted funding offers from our magnanimous government through its health agencies, wanting to maintain its independence. To the profession it is very important that it does so. In addition, doctors appearing before the tribunal have the assistance of the defence organisations, which through their nominated lawyers provide advice and representation. The tribunal also has a legal aid function for patients who wish to make claims and this enables accessibility without cost. Awards of costs against doctors are at present funded by the defence organisations. These can be substantial. In a sense, the doctor pays for the complaints against him and the funding of the disciplinary function through his own defence subscription which is in addition to his levies to the registration body.

Table 1 (page 14) illustrates the level of activity of the MPDC and demonstrates that this has increased quite dramatically during the period 1970 – 1990. Roughly speaking an increase of approximately 2000 per cent. The graph is self-explanatory. The increase can partially be attributed to the public's growing awareness and need for accountability. However in my view the major factor in this trend is the fact that post 1974 the disciplinary tribunal became the only forum where a patient's grievances could be aired. As you will note from the graph not all complaints go to a hearing. I'll explain in a moment how many of these complaints are resolved by a conciliation process thereby obviating the need for a formal hearing.

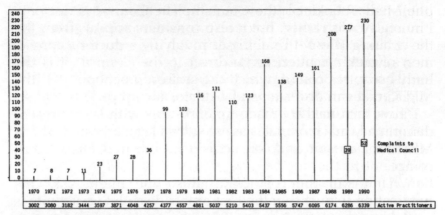

WRITTEN COMPLAINTS RECEIVED BY MEDICAL PRACTITIONERS' DISCIPLINARY COMMITTEE

(1) In recent years approximately 12% of written complaints have proceeded to a hearing before the Medical Practitioners' Disciplinary Committee, i.e. 1989-27 hearings, 1990-31 hearings.

(2) Approximately 12 million GP consultations per annum.

(3) Approximately 12 million hospital and specialist patient encounters.

Table 1

The Council, which has also been active in the last few years, considered 52 cases of alleged disgraceful conduct during 1990 and conducted five or six hearings. These complaints together with those to the MPDC give a total for the 1990 period of 280 or so complaints. This translates into a scale (according to my maths) of 1:23 doctors who have been on the receiving end of a complaint for that year.

It should be noted that the disciplinary machinery was not set up for the purpose of dealing with complaints in the no-fault environment. It was a structure already in place primarily to deal with complaints of a behavioural nature. Its function therefore changed with the advent of ACC and by evolution it increased its scope to cover all misdemeanours, such as failure to attend, clinical inadequacies, breach of confidence, failure to obtain informed consent, failure to advise of complications. The whole spectrum is now covered with the option to sue for negligence having been abolished. It's the only forum in which the complainant can have his or her day in court; where all the issues can be aired and addressed and adjudicated on.

14

As a result the disciplinary machinery in New Zealand is much more vigorous than that in Australia. The MPDC has published a booklet on how to complain about your doctor[2]. I must say it is rather disconcerting when you are sitting in the waiting room thumbing through the ubiquitous women's weekly magazines to come across this booklet: it hardly inspires confidence. But that is one of the steps the MPDC takes in order to explain the ease of accessibility.

I now turn to the practical operation of the system. The disciplinary machinery is set into operation by receipt by the MPDC of a written complaint. It sends a copy of the complaint to the doctor who is invited to give an explanation. That explanation is furnished to the MPDC which in turn sends it to the patient, in an endeavour to have the matter resolved. Obviously, there is an incentive for the doctor to frame his letter of explanation in conciliatory terms to enhance its acceptability. A fair number of complaints are resolved in this manner, with the complainants accepting the apology or the letter framed in a contrite way. On the other hand, if the doctor's explanation is rejected it steps up to the next level and the Chairman determines what happens next. The Chairman of the MPDC has the role of determining whether there's a case to answer, or whether the matter should be dismissed.

The MPDC has the wide powers of a commission of inquiry. It can subpoena witnesses; it can co-opt specialists to assist it, and it can hear any evidence, notwithstanding that the particular evidence would be inadmissible in a court of law (as hearsay) as long as the rules of natural justice are complied with.

The best way to portray the effectiveness of the MPDC, and its scope, is to relate several examples of cases I've been involved in recently.

A 20-year-old unmarried woman was referred to a large teaching hospital and at the outpatient department saw a consultant. She had unexplained pelvic pains. The consultant with his house surgeon examined her and resolved that she should undergo diagnostic laparoscopy (a look-and-see operation). She signed the appropriate consent and was booked for admission on a future date. Subsequently the house surgeon, attending to administrative matters, erroneously booked her in for a laparoscopic sterilisation (a

15

procedure quite different from the look-and-see operation). This mistake was perpetrated right through the system and the listed surgeon of the day sterilised the woman. The mistake was not realised until some days later when the general practitioner (GP) received the surgeon's report. The woman was awarded maximum compensation under the Accident Compensation Act 1972 but there was no regulatory punishment, or deterrent factor there.

Did the patient complain to the MPDC? She did not. She had her own reasons. You can imagine that all the doctors involved; the consultant who was a Professor elect, the surgeon and the houseman, including the anaesthetist, breathed collective sighs of relief. That relief was short-lived because the employing body, the Hospital Board, decided it would initiate a complaint. As a result there was a three-day hearing by the MPDC at which all doctors, save the anaesthetist, were found guilty of professional misconduct. That, indeed, was a salutary lesson and a sobering reminder. Publicity was given to the findings and caused some considerable disquiet. This illustrates that one does not need to be a plaintiff or a patient in order to make a complaint. Anybody can complain as is illustrated in that case.

The next example illustrates the effectiveness of the conciliation process of the MPDC. For the past two and a half years a female GP had managed a woman's breast lump and had checked it by mammography X-ray and assessed it as being benign. The X-ray showed no abnormality. Over at least this period it has been recognised in medical literature that it is not prudent to manage breast lumps by palpation and mammography only. It is well established that in order to exclude any question of a lump being malignant, the patient needs a biopsy and referral to a specialist. The GP managed it by mammography alone and it wasn't until it grew and became quite painful that the patient was referred to a specialist who immediately carried out radical surgery.

As can be imagined, the patient was extremely angry at being mismanaged; especially when other doctors readily articulated their criticism of the GP's management. Not surprisingly the patient sought legal advice and a written complaint was lodged with the MPDC and the doctor, in turn, was asked for an explanation. A rather distraught and worried GP came to see me requesting assistance from the

MDU. When I read the complaint, I gauged that a hearing might well be imminent, especially after I had spoken to some other doctors who told me that the management fell far short of what should be expected. I recount some passages from the letter of explanation the GP and I composed:

'To the Secretary of the Disciplinary Committee.

I realise that it is of little solace to Mrs X but I feel very bad about this matter. I was devastated to learn that the lump I was managing turned out to be a cancer. I cannot adequately express how sorry I am that Mrs X has had to go through this ordeal. It is only speculation but I do suspect that if I had not relied on my clinical findings supported by mammography, the X-ray, the cancer may have been detected earlier. In this case the course of treatment for Mrs X may have been less traumatic and the fear of spread may have been lessened. If only I had not put so much reliance on my findings and the mammograms. If only I insisted on a second opinion. There is little I can say to Mrs X in written form as I feel my sentiments are so inadequate. I contacted Mrs X as soon as I learned of the findings and she, quite understandably, made it very clear that because of me she had to go through hideous procedures and that her life had been put at risk...'.

One can only speculate that this letter of apology and contrition struck a chord with the complainant because the explanation was accepted and the matter did not proceed to the expected hearing. It was finalised by the Chairman of the MPDC who wrote to the doctor in these terms:

'I note that Mrs X has accepted your explanation, and I have given careful consideration to the issues. I am aware that the preliminary inquiries by this Committee may be a source of concern and distress to practitioners, however, they also and importantly, provide us with an opportunity to critically review aspects of our professional conduct. I am in no doubt from your letter that you have indeed reappraised your management of patients presenting with breast lumps. As I indicate in my letter to Mrs X's solicitor,

I am confident that you will exercise a more cautious approach in the future. I've accepted Mrs X's proposal that a notice should appear in a Medical Journal for education purposes reminding GPs not to place too much reliance on mammography as a means of diagnosing breast cancer. I valued your frank explanation to the Committee. I believe that this was both helpful in resolving the complaint and perhaps also avoided the necessity for a formal inquiry which would have been distressing for both Mrs X and yourself.'

I doubt that such a frank and contrite admission would have been made in a common law negligence environment. Overriding concern about liability and damages consequently would preclude a patient/plaintiff receiving such a humane, compassionate apology and self-criticism.

The next case I relate is an obstetric one which demonstrates the regulatory punitive powers of the MPDC, powers which any disciplinary regulatory body must wield in order to be both effective and be seen to be effective. An obstetrician managed a 30-year-old woman's first delivery in circumstances where risk factors during pregnancy and labour were high. Briefly, these included a 43 week duration of pregnancy, meconium staining during, at least, late first stage or early second stage, fetal heart slowing, fetal heartbeat undetected for a period of possibly 30 minutes, a prolonged second stage of three and a half hours or so, and the baby's head being visible on the peritoneum for nearly two hours. In spite of these factors, the obstetrician persisted with the planned course to deliver without intervention. After a difficult delivery, the baby was assessed as being brain damaged. The parents laid a complaint with the MPDC and a contested hearing took place.

After considering the evidence proffered by both sides the Committee concluded that any competent obstetrician and gynaecologist would have expedited birth in these circumstances by intervention. The tribunal found the doctor's management decisions to have been seriously lacking and that the failure to intervene was unreasonable, thereby constituting professional misconduct. The penalties imposed were robust: the doctor was censured; he was ordered to pay the maximum fine; conditions on practice were imposed including the Obstetrics Standards Review Committee conducting a case review of the next 20 deliveries and furnishing a report to the Chairman of the tribunal, such report to contain recommendations in order to address deficiencies in the doctor's mode of practice or to improve the mode of practice (an important and effective regulatory power). On receipt of these recommendations the MPDC should determine what steps were necessary to address them and to direct the doctor to undergo appropriate undergraduate training. The doctor was ordered to pay costs of $NZ15,000 (£5,000). The case details, without the patient's name, were to be published in the *New Zealand Medical Journal*. This resulted in the findings and criticisms being given wide currency in the general media. Robust findings indeed for this medical practitioner. Not surprisingly with this adverse publicity, as a private practitioner, the obstetrician's bookings dropped by two-thirds. On the other side of the coin, from the patient safety aspect the period of peer supervision and follow-up by the MPDC ensured that the deficiencies were remedied.

As an aside this leaves me to pose the question for purposes of comparison 'What happens to the incompetent doctor who is sued in the damages environment?'. Most likely this type of case would be settled out of court if it was so bad a case of negligence. Would the doctor, in effect, come to account? I suggest there are some beneficial features in our disciplinary field where the nature of the accountability process ensures that serious matters are better addressed than in the damages arena at present in operation.

Recently I spoke with the complainants involved in the obstetric case I have just referred to in order to assess from the other side, so to speak, how they felt about the disciplinary process. The husband, a journalist, was quite firm in his view that he and his wife had been well treated by the MPDC and given a very fair hearing. He said he was satisfied with the outcome, though, of course, (and one can imagine the reasons for this) he said he would have liked a lump sum of money as it would have been a greater help than what they got from the ACC.

The experience of cases such as these justifies me commenting with conviction that, with the abolition of damages litigation in New Zealand, standards in medicine have not dropped. The sword of Damocles is still there. (Though I could go as far as to say that now the spectre of Dionysius of Syracuse is sitting through a feast with possibly a sharper sword suspended over him with a hair that's even more frail than before.) I feel entitled to make these observations as one who has been up against the coalface with doctors in over 200 disciplinary cases and the one who's been privileged to advise at least 1,000, if not more, doctors facing complaints. I guess that makes me, quite justifiably, a hypochondriac when it comes to dealing with medicine for myself and my family.

I make no apology for being unequivocal in stating that a doctor has considerable fear of the prospect of coming before a tribunal made up of his peers. I've had many a doctor cry in trepidation prior to a hearing and many, in fact, also in relief after a hearing. I go as far as to suggest that a doctor would fear a disciplinary claim with its penalties on practice more than a negligence claim with its damages award.

Aside from erasure from the Medical Register or the imposition of limitations on practice, the penalty most feared by doctors is publication of their name in connection with adverse findings. Especially in our country – we're so small, everybody knows everybody – that's very much a factor. It's this publicity which doctors have difficulty in accepting. You may be surprised to know that up until now the disciplinary hearings have been held in camera and this fact has caused public disquiet. An awareness of growing public interest and the requirement to be accountable have resulted in a change to more 'open' hearings.

I suppose this apprehension overall on the part of respondent doctors is enhanced when it's borne in mind that the censure and findings of the MPDC constitute a public rebuke by members of the doctor's own profession. Those on the receiving end of malpractice cases may attempt to justify their position (and I'm sure that they do) on the grounds that the judge and/or jury were biased, they didn't understand – weren't really up on medical factors – that their decision was influenced by sympathy for the plaintiff, that they knew an insurance company was in the background. But who can question one's own peers? Such excuses are not available to those who are found wanting by a responsible body of their own peers.

20

Suffice it to conclude that a doctor contemplating disciplinary proceedings feels much keener in anticipation the cold breath of criticism that emanates from his colleagues. I have reiterated this and am convinced of it. It could be for a variety of reasons, being personally much closer to the action in the disciplinary field; not being one step removed or in with a group of other defendants. It is some years since I have been involved in malpractice cases, yet I recall the worst cases being settled and as a result the doctor's performance was not necessarily regulated and monitored in the future. What supervision, what sanction is there in the damages environment? However, I have to say that the disciplinary watchdog in my country has to have effective teeth and be seen to be effective. There are shortcomings: I've mentioned already the problem of the closed court, now it's open. In New Zealand there's currently a three-tiered system which is complex and clumsy, but now it's being revised. There's a new Bill before Parliament which aims to condense it to one tribunal providing it with more severe penalties. As it stands $NZ1,000 (£300) in anyone's language is a pretty puny monetary penalty and that is going to be increased dramatically.

For some time there has been a demand for much greater lay representation. At present there is only one lay person in each tribunal of between three and six doctors. It is expected that the new legislation will provide for a more balanced mix of four doctors and four lay persons. There's also been criticism of the fact that doctors sit in judgement of doctors and there's a move to have a retired judge or a senior barrister as chairman of the Committee, which will serve the need for some independence.

Recently these matters have been brought into issue and a long overdue revamp of the Medical Practitioners Act 1968 will remedy shortcomings which have become evident. This will lead to a more open public hearing and provide a disciplinary system which does not have the appearance of the 'old boy' network concept which did permeate our system for some time. Before these improvements were promulgated the cartoon on page 22 appeared in the local press. Although rather 'close to the bone' at the time it does not accurately depict the scene today, though that public perception has been slow to change.

This cartoon is reproduced with thanks to Mr Tom Scott, *Evening Post* (New Zealand).

Finally I highlight another form of accountability; an alarming and frightening development, at least for doctors in our country. This is in the form of medical manslaughter. I appreciate this is not unique in New Zealand as I realise that the criminal law is invoked in Britain and elsewhere in the Commonwealth as a means of holding doctors to account for negligent mishap causing death. What is unique in New Zealand however, is that the prosecution needs only to prove that death resulted from mere negligence. A breach of the civil standard of reasonable care is all that is required. A failure to exercise reasonable knowledge, skill and care while administering surgical or medical treatment is sufficient to justify a conviction for manslaughter. The test is no more than reasonableness.

In other jurisdictions there must be, in order to sustain a conviction, more than a mere breach of the civil standard which suffices in New Zealand. There must be a high degree of negligence. There must be gross or culpable negligence, recklessness, or an error of blatant and substantial magnitude. Not in New Zealand. The development and interpretation of the law in this respect has been quite different from that of other countries. The lower threshold of breach means that for many practitioners that Damocles sword I've referred to hovers over them by levitation only. You can imagine that doctors in disciplines such as anaesthetics, obstetrics, surgery and interventional radiology come within the category of those most at risk.

Decisions of the New Zealand Court of Appeal and the Privy Council have re-established the unique nature of New Zealand law regarding medical manslaughter. In the case of *R v Yogasakaran*[3] a woman had undergone gall bladder surgery. After the operation she was gagging on the intra-tracheal tube. The anaesthetist reached into the anaesthetic trolley drug drawer intending to withdraw Dopram. From the drawer marked 'Dopram' he took out a box and from the box an ampoule, drew up the colourless fluid and injected it. Unfortunately, and unbeknown to him, another person had placed dopamine hydrochloride in that drawer. The patient died as a result of having been injected with the wrong substance. The anaesthetist was charged with manslaghter and in summing up the judge indicated to the jury that the prosecution merely had to prove that there was an omission by the doctor to exercise such care as was reasonable in all the circumstances. The question was should the anaesthetist have taken the elementary precaution of reading the label? Was such a breach careless? The prosecution only needed an expert witness for the Crown to say one should read the label – of course. The doctor was convicted of manslaughter and discharged. The conviction was considered by the New Zealand Court of Appeal in order to test this low threshold of care. The Appeal Court confirmed that no more than ordinary negligence need be proven to justify a manslaughter finding. Likewise the Privy Council refused to interfere with the decision.

Another case, *R v McDonald*[4] also involved an anaesthetist convicted of manslaughter. Briefly the circumstances were that an Australian anaesthetist came to New Zealand to do a three month locum. He anaesthetised a boy who was having an appendicectomy. During the operation the surgeon exclaimed to the anaesthetist, 'the blood's a little cyanosed, with a blue tinge. More oxygen, please.'. The anaesthetist opened the tap to increase the gas flow on what he thought was the oxygen cylinder. The blood turned bluer. 'More oxygen', called the alarmed surgeon. The tap was opened further. The tragedy was that this anaesthetist was opening the tap of the carbon dioxide cylinder: not the oxygen cylinder as he thought. It had been 15 years since he had seen a carbon dioxide cylinder on a Boyle's anaesthetic trolley and it seems he did not see or register what he did not expect to see. The boy died of carbon dioxide poisoning. A prosecution for manslaughter was brought and the doctor, after a contested hearing, was convicted and fined. He, not being registered in New Zealand, was not subject to the processes of the Medical Council of New Zealand.

Currently I am representing a radiologist who has pleaded guilty to a charge of manslaughter *R v Morrison*[5]. In the course of performing a myelogram (an X-ray of the spine which shows up a prolapsed disc) his radiographer handed him a 20ml ampoule. Expecting it to be Iopamiro, the contrast agent, he withdrew the substance from the ampoule and injected it into the cerebral spinal fluid. 'Iopamiro' has blue lettering on the ampoule. In this instance the radiographer had handed to him an ampoule of 'Urografin', which is contraindicated for the sub-arachnoid space. The radiologist did not notice the wording Urografin set out in green lettering on the ampoule. The patient died from the toxic effects of the Urografin. The police laid a charge of manslaughter. The doctor feared, not so much the wrath or the punishment of a criminal process, but he feared more his own disciplinary body the Medical Council which could regulate, strike him off, or put impositions on his practice. Here he was facing a criminal charge and he said 'No, I want to plead guilty.' The Medical Defence Union offered him a full defence but he refused. He was convicted of manslaughter and discharged. It was quite extraordinary that the relatives of the deceased (a young man of 27 or so) wrote expressing their admiration at his courage in pleading guilty and their appreciation for his candour in making a full confession accepting responsibility. Very humbling.

I conclude by saying that it's been a pleasure addressing you. I hope I have given you food for thought that will lead to lively debate. I'm rather mindful of the two balloonists who were drifting along lost in cloud. Suddenly the clouds parted and below they saw a man walking with his dog.

24

'Hey, down there, where are we exactly?' they called. Surprised, the man with a dog looked up, 'Oh goodness, you're in a balloon about 300ft up.' Before there was any further exchange the clouds closed in and the dispirited balloonists drifted on. After a period of reflection one said to the other 'I bet that fellow down there was a solicitor.' 'How do you figure that?', enquired the other. 'Well what he told us on the one hand was perfectly reasonable and accurate but on the other it was totally bloody useless.'

I hope I've been a bit more helpful. Thank you.

References

1. *Green v Matheson* [1989] 3 NZLR 564.
2. *First Steps: How to Complain Against your Medical Practitioner.*
3. *R v Yogasakaran* [1990] 1 NZLR 399.
4. *R v McDonald* (unreported) High Court Christchurch T24/82.
5. *R v Morrison* (unreported) High Court Dunedin S7/91.

Mr Jan Sahlin

Separating accountability from compensation in Sweden

Mr Jan Sahlin

Legal Adviser to the County Councils and Member of the Medical Responsibility Board of Sweden

Mr Chairman, ladies and gentlemen. First of all I would like to express my sincere thanks to the MDU for having so kindly invited me to participate in this conference which indeed concerns a field of major importance. I am also happy to be in London again. This city is a close friend of mine since I got married here in 1957.

I take it that some international interest is attached to the legal system in my country for enforcing doctors and other persons' accountability, and patients' possibilities of being fairly compensated when something has gone wrong within health and medical care. The system has, of course, its merits as well as its imperfections. I hope that I shall be able to offer you a reasonable account without going into too many details.

I think it would be wise to start by summing up a few basic facts about Sweden so we all know what we are discussing and have a common base for our comparisons. The number of facts will not be repellent but might serve as a useful background.

Sweden covers 450,000 sq km, which is approximately twice the size of the United Kingdom as well as of New

Zealand. Its population is about 8.5 million people compared to 56 million in the UK and a little more than 3 million in New Zealand. There are about 25,000 doctors in Sweden, 15,000 of whom have passed specialist training. The number of nurses is around 75,000. Twenty seven million visits to doctors are registered every year; three per single inhabitant. Four million visits concern private practitioners, a number which may seem surprisingly small but which is a consequence of a health and medical care system where the dominant role is played by the public sector. The political responsibility is a legal charge for our 26 regionally elected county councils which all have taxation power. Supervision on behalf of the central government is a task for the National Board of Health and Welfare. Local political responsibility in each county council area is exercised by committees of various kinds designated by the county council. There is extensive freedom for county councils to decide the tasks entrusted to these committees. One effect of this freedom is that the political organisation in one county council area only very seldom is parallel to the corresponding organisation in the other ones. Apart from criminal offences, county council politicians are responsible only when facing their voters in general elections every third year. And it's not this kind of responsibility that is our subject at today's conference.

In Sweden it has for a long time been considered a matter of public interest to ensure that every individual receives good care and treatment when he is ill or has suffered an injury. Health and medical services, accordingly, are subject to quite penetrating public supervision. The practice of certain persons within health and medical care is conditional upon the practitioner passing an examination and being issued with a certificate. Such certificates are required not only for exercising the profession as a physician but also for dentists, nurses, midwives, psychologists, physiotherapists and a few other categories of health and medical personnel. Certification is regarded as a kind of quality assurance for these professional categories whose duties have such an important effect on individual security that their professional practice must be submitted to special stipulations. Rules about certification are combined with a legally-based prohibition of the practice of certain activities by non-certified persons in return for payment.

Public supervision of practitioners in health and medical care is also exercised through rules concerning disciplinary liability. Thus, in addition to penal liability which can be incurred by any citizen, special disciplinary liability has existed in Sweden for many years where medical personnel are involved. Besides disciplinary sanctions, questions of withdrawing certificates or cancelling authority to prescribe narcotics may arise.

The present legal rules concerning how matters of this kind are dealt within Sweden are given in the Supervision of Health and Medical Personnel Act which came into force on 10 January 1980. While certificates for practice in health and medical services are awarded by the National Board of Health and Welfare with reference to qualifying examinations stipulated for the various professional categories, questions of withdrawal of such licences and disciplinary liability are handled by a special independent authority, the Medical Responsibility Board, sometimes called the Health and Medical Services Disciplinary Board.

Here I must apologise for not being the right man to observe the more distinguished semantic differences between the words 'liability', 'responsibility' and 'accountability'. I hope I will be excused if I sometimes should use one of these words wrongly.

The Medical Responsibility Board is comprised of a qualified justice as its chairman and eight other members all appointed by the government for a period of three years. One member is nominated by the Federation of County Councils as the principal organisation of employers within the health and medical services. Three members are nominated by the three dominant unions in the same field, that is those organising the doctors, the nurses and the hospital attendants. And the remaining four members are, as a balance, nominated by the political parties in the Swedish Parliament.

It has been considered important that the Medical Responsibility Board has got this particular composition. It is a guarantee of independent judging and throws a light on all circumstances involved. There must not be too much room for professionals among the members to act in order to protect or just fraternally defend their accused colleagues. At the same time it's crucial that legal security of the personnel is taken into careful consideration. It is in the very nature of health and medical work that daily activities often cause complaints and suspicions. Personnel need protection against unjustified and groundless accusations and matters of a kind which would not regularly be brought to court. We believe that it is a good and appropriate system.

As far as revocation of certificates is concerned, the prerequisites would seem to be much the same as in other countries. Such measures are very often of more or less tragic background – mental illness, alcoholism or drug abuse. But certificates may also be withdrawn when there is gross malpractice or manifest unfitness. If the circumstances have changed when some years have passed, the cancelled licence may be given back to the practitioner. This is sometimes, but not very often, the case in our country.

If a person belonging to health and medical personnel intentionally or negligently fails in his professional duty and the fault is more than trivial, disciplinary sanctions may be imposed on him. Disciplinary sanctions comprise admonitions and warnings; the warning being the more severe sanction. This basic rule implies a few follow-up questions. What kind of responsibility and whose responsibility is tried by the Medical Responsibility Board? What is professional duty and what is not? Who belongs to health and medical personnel and who does not? And who is entitled to report to the Medical Responsibility Board?

The prime concern when implementing the provision given by law is to define the professional duties of medical personnel. In doing so, one has to consult legislation and statutory instruments as well as standing instructions, circulars and regulations, including local regulations of clinics and hospital departments governing the activities of various sections of the health and medical services.

The time given to me does not permit a deeper analysis or presentation of the more or less sophisticated borderline problems that may arise in this respect. The Supervision of the Health and Medical Personnel Act 1980 includes a general provision to the effect that health and medical personnel must exert themselves to provide the patient with

skilful and conscientious care as well as showing consideration and respect. Care must as far as possible be designed
and conducted in consultation with the patient who is
entitled to receive necessary information about his state of
health and alternative possibilities of treatment insofar as
this does not frustrate the purpose of care. Furthermore, the
general instructions for physicians require every physician
in compliance with science and proven experience to give
his patients advice and treatment which their condition
demands.

Thus, in the light of what has now been briefly passed in
review an assessment has to be made of the obligations
incumbent on medical personnel and on the occurrence or
otherwise of errors and neglect. This can involve a wide
variety of things ranging from inconsiderate behaviour or
insufficient information about the risks of complication to
incorrect diagnosis, surgery on the wrong side, or a mistake
in the course of a technically complicated operation which
takes a whole day to perform. But the actions must be within
the scope of health and medical care. If you see your doctor
drunk in a pub a thought or two may cross your mind when
you go to him the next time, but it is not a case for the
Medical Responsibility Board.

When we are facing the task of defining more precisely
which persons do belong to health and medical personnel,
the Supervision Act does not offer more than a very extensive overview. Very simply, the concept comprises everybody concerned with the care of patients in hospitals and
health centres or otherwise as certified professionals providing care privately as well as everybody assisting professional
practitioners in the context of care. Even a carpenter or a
caretaker employed at the hospital comes within this category, just as do unpaid hospital hostesses and cleaning staff
employed by cleaning companies contracted by the
hospitals, just to mention only a few examples. The reference to individual care of patients in the sense of the Act,
however, excludes public health service personnel, university teachers in the course of their teaching duties and social
insurance medical officers or medical advisers to municipal
authorities in these particular capacities.

The question of disciplinary liability is raised by the
National Board of Health and Welfare or by the patient

31

concerned. Should the patient have died or be in a state of health that makes it impossible for him to report the matter personally, notification to the Medical Responsibility Board can be made by a close relative. Complaints can also be filed by the Parliamentary Ombudsman and by the Chancellor of Justice. The cancellation of a certificate cannot be brought before the Medical Responsibility Board by an individual patient, in principle only by the National Board of Health and Welfare due to this authority's special supervisory duties. An accusation against a particular doctor or other person belonging to health and medical personnel must be delivered to him within two years from the event in question otherwise the case is statute-barred. If two or more separate events are reported simultaneously to the Medical Responsibility Board the effect of this rule may be that one of them eventually leads to a disciplinary sanction while the others are considered statute-barred and will not be dealt with at all. The discontented reporting patient often finds this a little peculiar and difficult to understand.

The Medical Responsibility Board's investigation of a reported case is very careful and usually takes some time before a decision can be made. Medical records and other documents are requested from the hospital referred to in the complaint. It may then prove necessary to obtain further documents from elsewhere. Both sides are entitled to inspect all documents in the case. The proceedings are almost always conducted in writing. The inquiry is accompanied by continuous consultations between the handling officer at the Medical Responsibility Board office and the referee who is a qualified medical specialist. Sometimes statements from the country's foremost experts in the field concerned are required to complete the references.

When the Medical Responsibility Board has made its decision in an individual case this does not always mean that the final word has been said. Decisions in cases concerning disciplinary liability or withdrawal of certificates may be contested by administrative appeal to an Administrative Court of Appeal. Appeals may be lodged by the National Board of Health and Welfare in order to safeguard public interests or by the reporting patient or by the reported doctor, or other reported persons belonging to health and medical staff if the decision has gone against them. Thus, a sanction may be reduced or a decision to revoke a certificate may be annulled by the court. Even the decisions made by the court may be subject to appeal, this time, to a final level, the Supreme Administrative Court. If a doctor, or whoever it is, wants his case to be reconsidered one more time, he must apply for a judicial review by way of certiorari (an order which transfers a case from a lower court to the high court for investigation into its legality). He cannot be sure that the Supreme Court will handle this last appeal.

I might add that minor problems which have arisen concerning, for instance, inconsiderate behaviour by the doctor or slight misunderstandings, also may be dealt with by local advisory boards appointed by the county councils themselves. Such matters may thus be handled in less bureaucratic ways without involving disciplinary sanctions.

Perhaps I should also add that the Medical Responsibility Board is financed by annual budget granted by the Parliament. No charge for its services is requested.

By raising questions of disciplinary liability at the Medical Responsibility Board patients quite frequently ask for economic compensation besides the wish to watch the failing doctor punished. Claims of this kind must always be declined by the Board, it simply lacks the legal competence to deal with questions of compensation. But this does not mean that injured patients cannot be compensated at all: they can, but according to rules stipulated in a quite different system. Before 1975 if a hospital patient in Sweden was injured by accident he could be compensated in accordance with the general principles governing tort law only if he could prove that some member of the hospital staff had been negligent and thus caused the injury. Only in a minority of cases was this possible and for that reason it was actually difficult for the injured person to get compensation if an unexpected complication occurred. According to tort law everyone who carelessly or negligently causes bodily injury or material damage is liable for the damages caused unless otherwise specified by law. The Act prescribes, furthermore, that anyone who has employees on his staff is liable for bodily injury or material damage caused by the employee through mistakes or negligence on official business.

An action for the recovery of damages on behalf of an individual is brought to court.

The main purpose of the present Swedish system is to create better possibilities for hospital patients suffering injuries to be compensated for loss. Before the no-fault programme began, patients in Sweden who were injured during medical care could not receive compensation for loss directly unless they were able to prove negligence on the part of the physician or the hospital. This situation was criticised because serious injury and economic loss could occur in cases in which fault could not be established and in fact compensation was paid in only a limited number of cases. Unexpected complications could not always be taken into consideration. It was generally felt that something had to be done and further discussion about the issue led to constructive negotiations between the Federation of County Councils, representing the county councils in their capacity as the principal owners and managers of hospitals in Sweden, and an insurance company consortium. An agreement was concluded in 1974 and the new system was introduced on 1 January 1975.

Swedish Patient Insurance has the character of liability insurance intended to cover liability in contract based on unilateral, generally applicable commitments by the health-care authorities. At the same time it will cover any liability that may occur from medical malpractice. However, the patient insurance includes to a higher degree than a conventional liability insurance a more distinct protection for the patient who has suffered an injury. The system has expanded and improved. It is continuously under further consideration and the terms are revised quite often. Initially the patient insurance covered only medical care provided by hospitals owned by the state or the county councils, today patient insurance contracts on equal terms have been concluded on a collective basis through which patient insurance also provides coverage for all privately employed doctors, dentists, physiotherapists and other healthcare professionals.

From a more general point of view the patient insurance now meets patients' actual need for compensation rather satisfactorily bearing in mind the type of injury and its consequences. It also provides a system where claims are handled in a more rational way than tort law permits and without unnecessary delay. Law suits with lengthy legal proceedings can be avoided as much as possible.

Sometimes the same case is reported both to the Medical Responsibility Board and to the patient insurance but one provides disciplinary sanction and the other compensation only. The investigations within the two systems may occasionally be parallel but the decisions are, in principle, independent of each other. It is not necessary that a compensation decision awaits a possible decision of sanction. The fact that patient insurance compensates a patient having suffered a treatment injury does not necessarily mean that the treatment itself was considered to be contrary to science and proven experience. The very mission of patient insurance is to decide exclusively whether an injured patient is entitled to compensation according to the rules adopted by those who have joined the system.

The patient insurance is in no way an activity of the national government and it is not part of the Swedish public social insurance system. The agreement is not required by law: it is altogether a private transaction and we feel that this domination of voluntariness is something very important indeed. Thus, patient insurance is a nationwide voluntary collective accountability insurance. It is also a no-fault insurance. The patient is compensated even when there is no negligence on the part of the hospital staff. It is financed by annual premiums paid by the county councils – using county council revenues from citizens – and other interested parties.

The presentation here of the terms of patient insurance must be rather brief and lots of details have to be omitted. Treatment injuries which are included in patient insurance can be classified systematically into five groups:

1. Injuries which have probably arisen as a direct consequence of an intervention leading to medical complications which could have been avoided if the treatment method had been applied in another way just as effectively.
2. Injuries which have led to severe disability or the patient's death and which have probably arisen as a direct consequence of treatment of a disease or an injury,

which untreated is of short duration or in any case cannot cause the patient serious inconvenience.

3. Injuries which have probably arisen or which could not have been prevented because what has been found at a medical examination performed with the help of technical apparatus has been incorrect or because observable symptoms of illness in connection with diagnostic intervention have not been interpreted with generally accepted medical practice.

4. Injuries which have been probably caused by an infection because the infection has been transmitted to the patient through medical intervention. This point has a number of exceptions which cannot be mentioned here. And finally;

5. Injuries which have probably been caused by accidents in connection with treatment or other acts performed by health and medical personnel, or accidents which have occurred during a conveyance of patient, or accidents which have occurred in connection with a fire or a similar event in a hospital or a health centre, or because of defective medical equipment.

A few exceptions from what is thus considered as a treatment injury are listed in patient insurance terms. One of them concerns the situation when an injury is a direct consequence of a necessary procedure including diagnostics or treatment of a disease or an injury which untreated is perilous or will probably lead to severe disability.

A claim for compensation cannot be raised, no matter how long a time has passed since the injury in question arose. Everyone claiming compensation according to patient insurance rules must do this not later than three years from the time when he first noticed the injury but never later than ten years from the time when the measure causing the injury was taken.

If an individual complainant does not accept the decision of the insurer regarding questions concerning his right to compensation he can have the case referred to an Advisory Claims Committee for an opinion. The Committee consists of six members, including a judge as its chairman, who are appointed by the government and the Federation of County Councils. The opinion is not binding on the patient or the insurer. Should the injured person not accept the recommendation, the Committee can invoke arbitration proceedings. In such a case the consortium of insurers should disburse the costs of arbitrators if the injured person's claims were not obviously unfounded. One of the arbitrators appointed by the parties to the dispute may request that a third arbitrator be appointed by the government.

Because the right to compensation is not bound to the question of whether or not the injury was caused by malpractice, but rather to questions concerning the unforeseeable nature of the complication, it ought to be possible to obtain a fairly accurate idea of risks which can be connected with different types of treatment methods. It is also possible to assume that medical personnel are more inclined to give information regarding complications that have occurred as this will influence eligibility for compensation in favour of the patient. Because the patient insurance does not search for scapegoats and normally does not make more detailed enquiries as far as the motives for the doctor's various treatment decisions are concerned, it is also the experience of the insurers' scheme that hospital staff and other medical personnel have become much more open to providing information concerning what in reality caused the injury than when malpractice alone justified compensation. Information passed to the patient insurance is confidential and is, in principle, not released to the authorities or to private persons.

As claims statistics which are computerised include details about basic illnesses, treatment methods, injuries, hospitals where treatment was performed, ages of injured individuals and the total cost of the injuries, it is clear that these statistics constitute a basis for analysis with regard to injury prevention. This material should be a niche for those searching for suitable possibilities to find precise medical information about complications which could have been avoided and which are normally compensable, as well as injuries which are considered impossible to avoid and which do not justify compensation through insurance.

So the two systems live their separate lives side-by-side without being joined in holy matrimony. One dealing with the punishing part when hospital staff members have failed in their professional duties and the other designed to try to provide reasonable economic compensation to patients suffering injuries when being treated within health and medical care. But it is not quite correct to say ' Oh, East is East and West is West, and never the twain shall meet, till Earth and Sky stand presently at God's great Judgement Seat'. The circumstances and facts being investigated within each system are often much in common and the systems can learn a great deal from each other. The important point is that an injured patient must have a fair possibility of receiving economic compensation from society independently of whether the injury is founded on medical malpractice or not.

The annual number of claims to the Swedish patient insurance represents today a little more than 4,000 injuries, of which, on an average, around 2,000 are considered compensable. About 300 cases are sent to the Advisory Claims Committee for further consideration. Again, figures of this kind must be related to a population of 8.5 million people and a total of 27 million registered visits to doctors a year. As a comparison, I might add that the number of reports to the Medical Responsibility Board amounts to roughly 1,300 every year. It is not possible to tell if such figures can be used as proof that complainants' wishes for compensation are greater than their wish to see a failing doctor hanged.

Thank you very much, Mr Chairman.

Discussion

Chairman

Thank you, Jan. Now the floor is open to all of you. And who would like to be first?

Dr Chris Ham
Fellow in Health Policy and Management, King's Fund College

I would like to ask two questions of both speakers, if I may? The first is to explore the link between the accountability processes and the compensation mechanisms. As I understand the Swedish system, if you pursue your claim for compensation there is then, as you said, no automatic link to the Medical Responsibility Board and as I understand it the reason for that is it encourages doctors and nurses to perhaps assist patients and claimants when they bring their claim for compensation. They may be deterred from doing so if the case is then reported on to the Medical Responsibility Board. I'd like to ask if the same sort of logic applies in New Zealand? In other words, when the ACC considers cases does it then keep those cases to itself, as it were, or report them on to the disciplinary tribunals we've heard about this morning? And if not, why? Is there some difference here we can explore between the two countries?

The second question is to compare and contrast whether we should have tort running alongside no-fault or whether we should go more down the New Zealand route where, in effect, the tort option has been closed off? I'd like to hear a bit more about the Swedish experience of how many claims are brought to tort alongside the 4,000 claims a year for no-fault.

Mr Jan Sahlin

About your first question, I didn't exactly note it as a question. I think you stated what I just said and there was no particular question concerning the Swedish system.

Chairman

I think just to confirm that that's the case.

Mr Jan Sahlin

Yes. And when it comes to the claims to the patient insurance I must ask for assistance from my colleague, Mr Mats Magnusson, who is also here and is better fit than I am to answer that kind of question.

Mr Mats Magnusson
Lawyer, Skandia, Sweden

Thank you, Jan. Mr Chairman, I am not going to talk so very long. I just want to introduce myself for the record. I am working at the Skandia Insurance Company, Sweden, which is one of the companies that form this consortium that runs patient insurance. And among other things I'm in charge of the legal proceedings taken – well, very simply, when someone sues the county councils. The question is here – how many cases there are taken to court instead of or parallel to the proceedings with patient insurance? And as far as I can say, for the last five years you could say we have about between 20 – 30 cases running in the courts. There are some more outstanding which can be settled out of court. Others we win and we lose some too. It's just the usual way of doing it. So it's about 30 cases a year. And we use help from lawyers outside the company, these cases are very bad publicity for the insurance company especially when there are children with brain damage, which is very interesting for the newspapers. I think that answered your question about how the Swedish system runs the proceedings in court.

Mr Christopher James

Well Chris Ham, the question as I understood it of me, on the New Zealand side, was whether any claim to the ACC can be 'switched over' or reported to the disciplinary tribunal with its accountability process. The answer in practice is no. There is very little switch-over or reporting. There is provision in cases where the ACC feels it has been unjustifiably and improperly claimed on for medical expenses. There is provision to pass that on to the disciplinary committee and a number of cases have been placed before the MPDC where a document such as a medical certificate has been fraudulent. For example, an opinion that the condition resulted from accident, when clearly it was congenital. I should explain that ACC as well as compensating patients, pays the medical fees. For instance, if you go ski-ing in New Zealand and you break your leg you have your medical fees paid whether you're a visitor or not. (That's why it's a good country to ski in.) As far as the comparison – Chris, I think the other question was the comparison – between running the tort and the compensation side-by-side. I don't want to tread on the toes of my compatriot, Sir Kenneth Keith. I think he'll be looking at the compensation side and he may have an answer for that as far as our experience is concerned.

Chairman

Is that sufficient, Chris?

Chris Ham

Can I have one supplementary? On Sweden, I wanted to make sure I understood the rules of the two tracks. If a patient or a relative decides to pursue a legal claim, does that then deny them the right to go to the patient insurance scheme?

Mr Jan Sahlin

No, not at all.

41

Chris Ham

So you can pursue a claim in the patient insurance scheme and take a legal case at the same time?

Mr Jan Sahlin

Yes, indeed.

Chairman

They can go both ways at once?

Mr Jan Sahlin

Yes.

Chairman

Both, or either, is that right? They have a choice of three there. Yes. Arnold.

Mr Arnold Simanowitz
Executive Director, Action for Victims of Medical Accidents (AVMA)

A few comments and a couple of questions, if I may? I thought that Christopher James' piece was extremely interesting and, of course, highly entertaining. Can I just start with a little criticism because, although I am now Director of Action of Victims of Medical Accidents, and I try to distance myself from being a practising lawyer because I'm not one, nevertheless, I thought that the way in which Christopher James pandered to the attitudes of the medical profession, certainly in this country, towards lawyers was not at all helpful. It is something that actually stands in the way of a bringing together of the patient's problems and the actions of the medical profession and, indeed, certainly in this country, with the help of our organisation, lawyers have done much more for the situation of victims of medical accidents than the medical profession has and we wouldn't be here today discussing these incredibly important problems if it weren't for lawyers. So I think to pander to that doesn't actually help because it's there, believe me, it's there.

Christopher James

As a visitor I may have to accept that, Arnold, and please don't misunderstand me. As a practitioner in this field and in addressing this topic I feel that sometimes provocation has a little benefit, in the sense that it causes one to reflect and enlivens debate. So it was there for that purpose, to provoke as well as to inform.

Arnold Simanowitz

Going on to your case, it seemed to me that what you had to say was actually the strongest case against the introduction of a system of no-fault compensation in this country in the way it has been approached, certainly in the two Bills that have been before Parliament in recent days, that I've so far heard. Because what we heard – to get anywhere near the sort of satisfactory system that patients would be looking for here – has taken something like 17 years. I have studied the situation in New Zealand since I've been involved in this organisation, for now something like nine years, and certainly what I've heard today is a vast improvement on what the situation was in the beginning. First, I think Chris James talked about the question of standards but I think he conveniently omitted to say that in the early days there was immense concern about dropping standards. There was concern over there and there was certainly stuff in the *British Medical Journal* over here, and concern amongst the medical profession about the drop in standards. I'm delighted to hear that that is beginning to be corrected. The other problem is the question of a public hearing. Any system of that kind must be public. It has taken 17 years for the influence of the general public to bring about that change – again, I'm delighted. What would the situation be here if we simply introduced no-fault compensation? And then there is the independence, the fact that you seem to be about to introduce a High Court judge or senior barrister as the chair is incredibly important. I think the cartoon you showed at the end is the perception the public would still have of the situation here, and it's absolutely vital to ensure that is seen to be independent.

43

Mr Christopher James

I agree with what you've said. In New Zealand it has very much evolved with the passage of time and it has taken rather too long for shortcomings to be addressed. We are two or three years late in the review of our Medical Practitioners Act and that's too long. But the parliamentary committee is moving and has moved as you've observed in response to the demands of the public and certainly that cartoon was apposite some years ago. Not so much now, because we are moving in the right direction, as you say.

Mr Arnold Simanowitz

I don't want to hog the platform, I know there are others who want to say things. But the main problem that we see is the question of the control of the medical profession and the two ways in which you've moved are very important. But what I really want to know, and this applies to Sweden and to New Zealand, is how does the patient know that something has gone wrong? If it is under the control of the medical profession there are many situations which are not reported and we've heard that there is no cross-over in New Zealand and there is no cross-over in Sweden. And we've heard from Mr Sahlin that the two things are kept separate and the fear of patients, of victims of medical accidents, in this country is that something will go wrong and it will not be reported. Again, I'm pleased to hear that in (New Zealand) the Hospital Board has reported cases. But in terms of the numbers, they're very small. In terms of the case example that you (Chris James) gave, we were talking about a well-known journalist, what about the people who are not articulate and well informed? What about incidents that are not quite as big as brain-damaged children, or not quite as big as some of the examples you have given? Will the patients without an advocate have the ability even to know that something has gone wrong which on one hand needs compensation and therefore should go down the one side, on the other hand needs disciplinary action and should go down the other?

Mr Christopher James

I'll follow that up first, Arnold. The question of how does the patient know? That question could be asked, of course, of any system – a common law damages system or a no-fault system. This recently has been addressed by the appointment of patient advocates. We also have a Bill before Parliament at the moment for the introduction of a Health Commissioner. All these are slowly, maybe belatedly, moving along that line. Much of this movement to ensure a greater awareness of greater accessibility has resulted from a rather well-publicised case – an enquiry into the activities of some senior obstetrician/gynaecologists at the National Women's Hospital and as a result of what we call the Cartwright Enquiry, much has evolved. Some feel we have gone too far, and that is certainly being looked at in many of those areas that you have raised which have been shortcomings in our system. So there are agencies being set up at the moment in order to provide better information. Over the years, there's been greater publicity given to these cases and that little booklet I mentioned leads to a much greater awareness amongst the public of their right to complain. In fact, many complain in order to find out what happened. The disciplinary forum is used to ascertain whether something went wrong. And that I think is quite healthy. It doesn't cost patients anything. There is ease of accessibility. At the moment we're improving further on this 'how do they know' element by the introduction of a Health Commissioner and by the patient advocates.

Chairman

I wasn't sure I understood the point about a drop in standards. Is that right, there was a drop in standards?

Mr Christopher James

Of course there was a fear that there would be a diminution of standards if you take away the Damocles sword – the threat of being sued. One can glibly say that in New Zealand a doctor, as far as money terms are concerned, can act with immunity and impunity. But I have not, in my experience, seen that drop. There still remains medical professional pride, which I have respect for and that alone keeps a considerable number of doctors on the rails, I suspect. There's nothing to show that there's been a drop in standards, though that graph showed a twenty-five-fold increase in complaints. It's not so much that there's been more medical accidents or negligence but that there's become an increasing awareness of accountability.

Chairman

Jan Sahlin, in Sweden, how does the patient know that something has gone wrong?

Mr Jan Sahlin

Well it's quite obvious – there are at least a number of cases each year which are not reported either to the Medical Responsibility Board or to the insurance and the causes of why this is the case may be of various kinds. If you have a family doctor who has been your personal doctor for the last 25 years and he fails in something, one or another of the visits you make to him, it's not possible for you to report him to a disciplinary sanction; you just don't do these things – this is understandable. And therefore the statistics concerning the reported cases are not always reliable to cover every case which has happened over a year.

Mr Arnold Simanowitz

I wasn't really talking about cases of family doctors. I was talking about more serious matters, and Christopher says that this is a problem under any system. It is a problem under any system and that's why our organisation is now pushing for something which some bodies have mentioned in the past which is a medical inspectorate. So you get something which is pro-active and not re-active. Because, although I'm not attacking the professional pride of the doctors or their honour in any way, if you take my favourite example which I use both in local compensation and for accountability is the damage which is caused to the ureter in, for example, hysterectomy. Until a few years ago, that was considered an acceptable complication and nobody would have done anything about it on the compensation side or under the accountability side. There was one famous doctor I know of who was well-known for the damage he caused to the ureter on almost every occasion, but the doctors considered that that was acceptable. So that wouldn't have been investigated, and not being a doctor, I don't know how many other situations of that kind are floating around. But they are, and in New Zealand we have been contacted by patients' organisations asking us for advice on how to set up an AVMA in New Zealand because they do not feel they are getting the satisfaction they need. So that was the import of my question – how do patients know?

Mr Christopher James

Arnold, satisfaction in money terms or accountability terms on that ..?

Mr Arnold Simanowitz

I think it's in both. Money terms is a problem but something that presumably we'll be addressing this afternoon. But in accountability they still feel that the medical profession has this wall of silence after all that you've been telling us and I think what you've said is a great improvement and it's certainly something that we can learn from here. But we've got to be very careful not to think that introducing it in that way, without learning a lot of the lessons that you've learnt and many more, will be the answer.

Chairman

Yes.

Prof Jean Louis Portos
Le Sou Médical, France

I would like to ask both speakers a question on what is the percentage of claims for compensation which are rejected in both countries?

Mr Christopher James

So as far as the answer for the New Zealand side is concerned, I would ask Sir Kenneth Keith whether he has that type of statistic, because, sir, I don't. Sir Kenneth – what percentage of claims do not get compensation?

Sir Kenneth Keith

I'm afraid I don't have any specific figures. The general figure is very small: three or four per cent.

Chairman

So three or four per cent for New Zealand but it isn't medical claims specifically. Thank you. Sweden?

Mr Jan Sahlin

As far as Sweden is concerned, I must again turn to Mr Magnusson to assist me because I don't have the figures myself.

Mr Mats Magnusson

We are talking about rejected claims to patient insurance – if you take away the dentists who are insured in a special way due to the system – you could say that we reject a little more than 50 per cent of the cases. A little more than 2,000 cases are rejected. But to understand why they are rejected, you must also know a little bit about the system (I'd like to come back to that a little bit later) because I have a feeling that 'no-fault' means different things to different people. But in this no-fault system that we have in Sweden we exclude cases that are on a very low level of damages. I mean I think the border is about £70, isn't it? Yes. £70 is the lowest limit – if it isn't over £70 we reject it. There is also this, what Mr Sahlin talked about, the question of the time in which you have to take the problem to the patient insurance. It is up to three years after you have noticed the result or damage. That's a little bit lower than the usual ten years in court cases according to tort law in Sweden.

Prof Jean Louis Portos

Thank you very much. But even taking into account the system, it is – I think it is something we might look into later in the discussion, the difference between four per cent and over 50 per cent is something which is striking.

Chairman

Yes.

Dr Ronald Mann
Royal Society of Medicine

I'd like to make one comment and ask three quick questions, if I may, Chairman? The comment is that Arnold Simano-witz said that what's happening is because of what the lawyers have done and I think he's right. It's what they've done so badly that's causing things to happen. At least, the legal process is so unsatisfactory from the point of view of many patients that a lot of people are beginning to ask whether this isn't something that really needs to be changed? I don't mean that too flippantly, it's not the lawyers, but the legal process itself that we suffer from is the real trouble.

My three questions are: would the two speakers tell us what were the motivating causes of the change in their countries? There is clearly in the medical profession in this country quite a widespread wish to see change. There is a great reluctance in the political administration to change. What actually precipitated it? Wherefrom came the great forces that must have led to these changes in these two countries?

And the second question is that it's often said that one of our difficulties if we introduce a no-fault compensation scheme with a parallel accountability machinery in this country, would be that this has worked only where the schemes provide mere top-up payments, quite modest in proportion to existing very substantial social security bene-fits. Is that the view of these two speakers, that in fact what you can give under an affordable no-fault scheme is really quite modest in comparison with what they would get under tort action?

And the last question is about brain-damaged babies who have already been mentioned two or three times. Many people feel that the number of brain-damaged babies and the kind of benefit given to them would be – if any similar benefit was brought about – enough to defeat a no-fault compensation scheme in this country and what has been the experience with brain-damaged babies and claims in these two important countries?

49

Mr Jan Sahlin

I must confess that it was a little difficult for me to understand your questions.

Chairman

The first one was what was the motivation for change in the first place? Why was the scheme introduced?

Mr Jan Sahlin

To offer better possibilities for the patient to get compensation without having to prove negligence or malpractice on the part of the hospital staff.

Chairman

And had that been – was that sudden or had it been developing over a long period?

Mr Jan Sahlin

It had been developing over a long period.

Chairman

The second one was would a no-fault system only function where it is essentially only a top-up to an existing extensive system of social benefits since the amounts awarded are likely to be quite small relative to tort?

Mr Jan Sahlin

I'd like to answer very simply, yes.

Chairman

And I'm sorry, Ron, you'll have to remind me of the last question?

Dr Ronald Mann

The last one was about brain-damaged babies.

Mr Jan Sahlin

We have not had many cases in Sweden so far going to court decisions, so we must await further developments before it is possible to give a satisfying answer to this question. I don't know if you, Mats, would like to add to this.

Mr Mats Magnusson

Yes. The question is very reasonable. The Swedish system of compensation covers through the no-fault scheme exactly the amount of money you get even if you go to court and furthermore, a little bit better when it comes to compensation for permanent disability. That's our construction of it. We wanted to be able to say to people that it's not a good idea to go to court, come to us instead. You're better off with us. And that can be discussed, if it is good or not? My personal view is that it isn't. But you must have a substantial social security system to support this. Our costs for losses of earnings are very low – what we mostly pay out is non-financial losses. Pain and suffering, losses – damages for permanent disability and costs. So I think you must have a substantial social security system. Then to brain-damaged children. We pay compensation for that but the problem that has arisen recently is that there have been claims for substantially 'better care' here. And the fears are that we will create an A and B system for caring for children, where the A system is for those children who can lean back on an insurance company and B is for the poor child who is born without that specific company to rely on, the so-called normally damaged child, where you can't find anything that has gone wrong because the Swedish system of patient insurance does not cover things that are unavoidable. You must remember that. Things that don't have anything to do with what a doctor or a nurse has done or has not done, when the complication, as we say, couldn't have been avoided, well then there is no compensation. So that is what I mean by the so-called no-fault scheme in Sweden.

Mr Christopher James

Dr Mann, it's rather unfortunate that the question you asked in a sense has more application for this afternoon in the compensation side and I'm sure you'll find your queries addressed there. Suffice it for me, at this stage, to indicate that a major problem with the New Zealand scheme was that the money level has not kept up with inflation. In 1974 with the stroke of the bureaucratic pen one's God-given right (or at least from Magna Carta) to sue your fellow man for the wrong done on you was taken away and was replaced by a social contract. And that social contract provided that you were to receive compensation at a certain level adjusted to keep pace with inflation. It has not done that. I should point out that our scheme is not just confined to compensation. It's directed in three areas: education and prevention; compensation, and rehabilitation. So it covers a greater spectrum than compensation alone. The maximum compensation that can be gained for pain and suffering together with loss of enjoyment is NZ$27,000 (£9,000). In 1974 it was a little less but it has not moved up. That's one of the criticisms of our system, too much interference by the sticky finger of the politician. You get some sort of manipulation to keep tax down and that, of course, does mean there is a deprivation of the monetary compensation level.

To keep it in perspective I should mention other aspects, the brain-damaged baby, for example, or the quadriplegic or paraplegic. There is an earnings-related compensation which is awarded for life, and this, in effect, amounts to a huge sum of money. If one is deprived of the capacity to earn income because of injury, regardless of fault (it might even be skiing), that is compensated for at a level of 80 per cent of a certain figure which gives a maximum of something like NZ$75,000 (£25,000) for life. I have a friend who, as a law student, injured himself while skiing and became a tetraplegic. As well as all medical and rehabilitation costs being met, the ACC converted his house to facilitate movement in a wheelchair. His car controls were changed and he was provided, in effect, with a pension for life.

Now the brain-damaged baby could come into that same category. I mentioned the case of the complainant whose baby was brain-damaged at birth (because of lack of intervention by the O & G specialist) who said that he would much rather have had a large lump sum of money in a sense to compensate. Overall I feel that the compensation level is small compared to what the damages award or settlement could have been in another environment. Though in the common law environment you need to prove fault in order to receive that. How many cases succeed where you can prove that and they are not an all-or-nothing lottery?

As far as the philosophy is concerned as to why we did it, I think that may come through this afternoon, Dr Mann. Does that address the points you've raised?

Dr Ronald Mann

Very helpful.

Chairman

Yes, Julia.

Rabbi Julia Neuberger
Chairman, The Patients Association

I'm also a Fellow at the King's Fund. First, a comment which is that, like Ron Mann, I think that we've been very aware that patients, quite apart from the medical profession, have been extremely dissatisfied with the legal process as it operates in this particular area. And we receive a large number of patient complaints and concerns and we refer quite a lot of them on to Arnold Simanowitz, obviously. But it was particularly interesting to hear from Chris James about the way that individual doctors apologise and the sorts of letters that they might write. Because what is said to us time and time again is that people do not want to go, particularly through complicated proceedings, or necessarily wish to go into any form of formal proceedings at all, but they want to get some form of apology and expression of concern from the medical practitioners. And certainly in this country as things have been standing at the moment, the view of the defence organisations has been fairly negative about expressing apologies on the basis that they could, in fact, consist in being an admission of liability of some kind and therefore, that was a very important point which you raised.

And now I have two specific questions. One is that when, in the New Zealand system, you were describing the way that the change has just come about, I think, of having a retired judge as chairman of the disciplinary committee and

indeed, having four lay members along with four professionals, is that purely as a result of all the flak surrounding
the Cartwright Enquiry? In other words, did it need a fairly
major political scandal to ensure that? And second, do you
think that if we were to go for some no-fault compensation
system in Britain – which the Patients' Association have
backed in a fairly broad way – if we were to do that, would it
be possible to use the examples of the change over the years
of your system to say there would have to be a system with
equal lay and medical representation on any board considering such issues?

I've got many more but I'll leave it there for this morning.

Mr Christopher James

Those are two very interesting points you raise. The first
comment you made with regard to the apology. The in-
formal resolution phase provided by the MPDC process
allows such sentiment to be expressed and on many occasions I have seen patients accept an apology and express the
wish that the matter proceed no further. However, one may
wonder to what extent the inability to seek a large dollop of
damages money influences this acceptance of the doctor's
apology. 'What is the use of a disciplinary hearing to me,
when I've got three children to feed?' 'How is it going to
help me if I merely have the satisfaction of seeing that doctor
eat crow, or that doctor be found guilty of some conduct
unbecoming, unprofessional misconduct? There may be
satisfaction in a vindictive way, but it doesn't actually help
me on the monetary side.' And this is where we have the
accountability, of course, and the compensation separated.

I would think – looking back on it now – that it's rather
scandalous that we had in New Zealand a closed shop
system run by doctors for doctors. However, there has been
a positive response to public pressure. But in the eyes of
many it has been rather late and I think if there was any
consideration of going down our track one would have to
take very strong cognisance of the shortcomings, the very
obvious shortcomings, that we have experienced. You ask
whether it was the Cartwright Enquiry which triggered this?
As far as having a non-medical person as a chairman (and it
hasn't been resolved yet – it may not be) the medical profes-

sion is quite keen on maintaining its own chairmanship. Depending on that, we'll see what happens fairly soon. An agreed proposal for change has been in the political system for about four years. Frequent changes of government in our country have not helped, you understand. But the Cartwright Enquiry certainly did focus on a number of issues some of which highlighted the need for improvements in the accountability process. A number of doctors have commented on what a change there has been in New Zealand in the medical climate as a result of this Enquiry and its revelations. There was Professor Bonham and Professor Green, the doyens of the O & G field in this highly respected teaching hospital. Criticism of Professor Green's management and treatment of patients was given wide currency in the media as a number of patients reviewed their trust in their own doctors saying in effect 'There's old Dr X, I've trusted him for years. Goodness! If that professor who was held in such esteem is wrong, I wonder if I'm being given the right treatment by my own doctor'. So it's created a climate where more questions are being asked. One might say created a greater accountability and awareness. So possibly this Enquiry has hastened changes that need to be addressed.

Rabbi Julia Neuberger

Can I just add a supplementary? Just to ask you when you think the issue will be resolved? As to whether there are going to be four lay members and a lay chairman?

Mr Christopher James

It's either four or six. The Bill is still being debated. But there are a number of items that have come out at the moment – you might have seen them – 'Should doctors play at being judges?'. And some of the concern comes from doctors themselves, saying 'I would rather have a non-medical person passing judgement on me. I mean I don't think much of that doctor, I was at university with him. Why should he be passing judgement on me?'. Some feel it would be much more acceptable if it was a legally-trained chairman, assisting in the assessment of credibility and the questions of evidence and the like, rather than a doctor.

Dr Ian Field
Secretary, British Medical Association

I think perhaps in a situation like this I need to declare an interest and it's not the obvious one. As a young man, my wife and I lost our first child and it was very apparent to the pair of us that the reason for the loss was an element of medical negligence. The fact that the doctor concerned felt able to indulge in fairly severe self-criticism openly with us did much to reassure us that there was no point in pursuing it because, however emotional we were at the time, there was no point in pursuing it because we felt the lessons were being learned and carried forward. That has actually been a very important factor in my own belief, for the last 15 years, that we really must get away from the tort-based system in this country. We think it's harmful, unpredictable and unjust. We believe, in fact, that it breaks down the relationship that there ought to be between a doctor and a patient and encourages concealment just at the very time when openness ought to be the order of the day.

I, frankly, have been encouraged by what I've heard from New Zealand today. It seems to me that the system of separation of compensation/accountability does allow those who investigate accountability to concentrate more on the process than the outcome because I feel all too frequently it's the nature of the outcome in a tort-based system which is generating what's going on – there is not really a proper examination of the process. I don't share Arnold's fear that what has taken 17 years to evolve in New Zealand will necessarily take 17 years to evolve in the United Kingdom. If we could separate the two I believe that we have shown ourselves as Brits in a number of fields in this country ready to learn from the lessons that other people have developed. We don't need to re-invent the wheel from the beginning. And so I don't actually feel that that delay is inevitable here.

But I think also times are changing in this country. It's time we moved away from assuming that what would have happened ten years ago under traditional attitudes, both from patients and the profession, won't necessarily happen in the future if we move into a new system. I would like to put just one question to the two speakers: given your experiences, would you for one instant consider going back to a tort-based system?

56

Mr Jan Sahlin

In Sweden we have taken a firm decision not to revert.

Mr Christopher James

As a personal injury lawyer who acted for insurance companies, the answer would be yes. (Laughter.) Slightly tongue-in-cheek; the serious answer would be no. There is no need for you to re-invent the wheel. New Zealand pioneered the full implementation of 'no-fault' and you can learn from our pitfalls and mistakes. You can draw on our experience. What prototype car was ever highly successful right from the start? And New Zealand really has been the prototype and it has taken some time to develop and iron out the rattles, the understeer and other deficiencies. It's fair to say that the NZ scheme is far from perfect but 17 years of operation means you have a working example to observe and criticise.

Dr Ian Field

Can I just come back with just a small piece of information which may not be generally known but the British Medical Association is actually part of a group called the Toronto Group which consists of most of the Nordic countries – Holland, Britain, Ireland, New Zealand, Canada. What is interesting is that in the group there is increasing interest in all those countries in moving away from a tort-based system and towards so-called no-fault compensation with a totally different system for accountability.

Mr Christopher James

Dr Mann asked and I always wondered as an individual :17 years, if it was such a good thing, why has it taken so long? We had the Pearson Commission[1] look at us years ago. It seems that other countries have taken considerable time to become aware of the benefits of a no-fault system.

Mr David Bolt
Chairman, British Medical Association Working Party on No-Fault Compensation

So much of what I wanted to say has been very successfully said by the (BMA) Secretary which saves time. I just wanted to make a comment en passant about the remark made by our New Zealand guest about the doctors who would prefer to be investigated by a lay body than a medical one. It is, of course, very much easier for a medical practitioner to pull the wool over the eyes of a lay body than over his medical colleagues. I perhaps have some slight bias as for some years I chaired the Professional Conduct Committee of the General Medical Council and I was always conscious of the fact that my colleagues on the committee questioning doctors who where, so to speak, in the box, were very, very much more searching and very, very much more damaging than were lay advocates.

However, one other point and I will stop. It seems to me that one of the things that confuses us in this country terribly, is this firm belief that the tort system represents a method of accountability. This, of course, is absolute nonsense. The serious cases – the ones with serious evidence of negligence or incompetence will never see the courts. The doctor concerned suffers no adverse publicity. And whatever sums of money are involved will be picked up either by health authorities through NHS indemnity or by the defence organisations, so the damage he receives is absolutely minimal. So to cling to the tort system on the grounds that to lose it would diminish doctors' accountability really, Mr Chairman, this is a fundamental error. I would so like to see that idea dropped and a critical look taken, perhaps, at how to make accountability in relation to medical mishap more effective, because at the moment it is totally ineffective. There is no system which gathers up cases involving actual negligence, let us say, among these to be looked at critically by the authorities. It doesn't happen. Clearly, if you had a central machinery dealing with no-fault compensation you would at least have a structure which could look at it. Now, I'm very well aware that Dr John Wall would tell you that this would be a great mistake and that the two should not have any contact with each other and this is a perfectly valid argument, but nevertheless at the moment we don't try to look at the mistakes that, shall we say, end up with substantial out-of-court settlements and therefore if we move from the tort system, we move forward, Mr Chairman, not backwards.

Chairman

Well thank you all very much. Thank you, both Jan Sahlin and Christopher James, very much for this morning.

References

1. Lord Pearson. Royal Commission on Civil Liability and Compensation for Personal Injury. London 1978 HMSO Cmnd 7054 I-III.

Compensation: is there a better system?

Sir George Pinker

*Immediate Past President of The Royal College of
Obstetricians and Gynaecologists*

During the morning we heard discussions about the system of accountability and this afternoon's question is compensation: is there a better system?

Sir Kenneth Keith from New Zealand will be talking about compensation as seen in New Zealand's scheme and Dr Barry Manuel of Boston will be talking on what may happen if there's no change in the UK system. I have a feeling that that particular presentation may be X-rated.

The present system of compensation now produces very large sums of compensation for a very few of the patients who have similar needs following illness, accident or the morbidity of medical and surgical treatment. And this is one of the things that worries us very much. For a small group there is a massive recompense but the need still exists for many others who have no claim against an individual medical officer and have to still fund and look after a debilitated child or a relative without that support. And I must say that any scheme which we eventually devise I think must take into account all those who need, rather than all those who are victims of one or another accident.

The average time of nearly five years, and often as much as ten years to complete complex legal claims, is itself a marked feature of the present system. And in 1989 there were eight cases which went back 20 or more years. How one can ever relate to the practice as it was then and equate decisions on the inadequate notes and the style of practice at that time, is almost impossible to conjecture.

In 1988 I went with two of my colleagues from the Royal College of Obstetricians and Gynaecologists to alert the Department of Health through the Chief Medical Officer (CMO) to the impending doom we saw coming for obstetrics in particular. I shall ever be grateful to Sir Donald Acheson for his listening ear and the fact that he prepared as best anyone could to meet with the problems should they arise. As you know, another defence organisation suddenly landed us with differential subscriptions which looked as if they were going to put obstetricians into a net of £5,000 a year subscriptions. This was so unacceptable to the specialty that the Department of Health saw the problem looming large and urgently and brought in NHS indemnity to try and sort the matter out. I think it's only a temporary holding operation because health authorities who have to fund claims are going to find that with the level of claims that exist at the moment they're going to have to close wards to pay for compensation of one or two major cases a year should they arise. And with the level of claims which is going through at the moment each hospital is going to have one major claim a year on average, if not two.

One of this afternoon's speakers, Dr Barry Manuel, wrote in the *New England Journal of Medicine* last year that no-fault compensation should be considered for urgent introduction in the United States where patients were suing themselves into second-class medicine[1]. I'll be interested to hear him elaborate on what could happen if the British public and the medical profession went further down the litigation trail in the footsteps of American colleagues. Dr Wall took part in the Bar Conference three years ago and noted the views of certain judges. Mr Justice Hirst was the first to award £1 million to a patient in the High Court in Britain. He told the assembled judges and lawyers that he thought a system of no-fault compensation would be a great improvement[2].

61

Another High Court judge, Mr Justice Beldam, said that society in Britain was moving towards a social compensation scheme of the type introduced in New Zealand. In return for the surrender of legal right of action anyone suffering injury must still be entitled to benefits for loss of earnings and personal injury and pay. At the same conference Mr Justice Ian Kennedy described the present system as coarse, clumsy and to a certain extent a lottery but still thought it was fairer than any other available system. The Lord Chancellor referred to the Bar as a profession struggling to adapt. Every profession is becoming acutely aware that its role in society can only be justified by careful attention to the interests of the public as a whole.

However, today is not the occasion to discuss the agonising debate about causation and the too-ready assumption that the obstetrician caused congenital disabilities simply because they are diagnosed in a new-born child in whose delivery he has been professionally involved. And it's interesting to read Sir Donald Acheson's distillation of his thoughts over the years in the William Powell lecture which he gave to the College of Midwives on this subject in 1990, and his conclusion is that the upward trend of litigation for cases of cerebral palsy is both unjustifiable in the face of present evidence and unacceptable in terms of its potential consequences to the quality of the care available to pregnant women. As far as scientific evidence is concerned it is now clear that perhaps as few as ten per cent of cases of cerebral palsy are due to asphyxia during delivery; that in an even smaller proportion could actions of commission or omission by the attendant have altered the outcome. In these circumstances, in any particular case of cerebral palsy, the balance of probabilities must start in favour of the obstetrician and against the plaintiff. It also follows that in future, cases where negligence is proved should be distinctly uncommon and they should be a small fraction of the number being brought forward at present. Would that it were so.

The European Commission in Brussels is producing a whole sequence of drafts which may be imposed on national governments about compensation for alleged faulty professional services[3]. Initially health was lumped together with those of construction engineers and accountants. We, in

Britain, have an opportunity to consider whether a better system is available and we shall hear this afternoon about another system of compensation. Thank you.

References

1. Manuel B M. Professional liability – a no fault solution. *N Engl J Med*, 1990; 322:627–31.
2. Bar Conference 1–2 October 1988, London.
3. Council Directive C12/8; 18.1.91.

Sir Kenneth Keith

Compensation in New Zealand 1974–1991

Sir Kenneth Keith
President of The New Zealand Law Commission

I thank you very much, Mr Chairman, ladies and gentlemen. It's a great privilege for me to stand here today to tell you something of the New Zealand Accident Compensation Scheme. I wondered when I was listening to my compatriot whether I should try to compete with his opening. I decided I would not but I thought I might mention a common structure of a Maori greeting on an occasion like this. That greeting would usually mention first the place where we are meeting and the traditions surrounding that place. I received a very considerable impression of that as I came into this superb building today. It does bring home to someone who is, in part, from a very new country a real feel of the depth of the tradition and of the great things that have happened in the Royal College of Physicians, this place we are in today. The second and related thing is to talk about the people who went earlier and contributed to that greatness. And the third, and in some ways the most important thing, is the people who are here today and the people we are talking about. There is a standard Maori proverb, which even those who are as poor at the language as I am use, which ends by referring to the most important thing – 'The people, the people, the people'.

Coming to my topic, I want to consider compensation for people who are injured under three headings.

The first is: why was the New Zealand Accident Compensation Scheme adopted and what are its main elements? That question was raised this morning in a number of contexts.

Second, how does this scheme operate in practice? And in particular, how does it operate in the area of medical malpractice or 'medical misadventure', which, as Chris James indicated, is the New Zealand statutory expression. The cost element is an important part of that second heading.

And third, given recent controversies about the operation of the scheme including the costing, what is to be made of proposals for the extension or modification of the scheme – because I think some of you will know of the current reviews, debates and arguments. I notice for instance that in the debate in the House of Commons here there were some references to the current state of the New Zealand scheme[1].

There's a preliminary point which a number of people have already touched on but perhaps it's worth running over again. It is this: why should the experience of a small country on the other side of the world be of interest here? Another reason for asking the question is that the scheme was adopted before many recent developments in medical negligence law, changes in attitude towards professions, and changes in medical technology. Your organisers have acted on the basis that that experience is relevant. I will try to support their confidence. You will be able to judge whether they were right.

Let me mention two studies, one from a good time ago and one which is more recent, which I think do show the value of comparative study. The first study was done almost a century ago. It was a study of employers' liability laws and related insurance regimes in 40 different jurisdictions in the British Empire, America and Europe[2]. The introduction to that study was written by a London barrister. It is interesting reading and sounds very contemporary. He said that the study led him to record the growing conviction that the only satisfactory approach to these questions of employers' liability was to separate compensation for those who were

66

injured from precautions against accidents and enforcement of safe practices. They were, he said, two quite distinct matters which should be handled separately.

The other comparative study is that which was done just three years ago by Professor Walter Gellhorn, an eminent American legal scholar, who in his ninth decade came to New Zealand to look at the Accident Compensation Scheme. (In his seventh decade he had come to New Zealand to look at the Ombudsman, again as part of a comparative study[3].) This excellent article compares medical malpractice litigation in the United States with medical misadventure compensation in New Zealand. He addressed the question of the relevance of the New Zealand experience and answered it with the famous statement – at least famous within the United States – about the federal system: 'A single courageous state, it has been said, may, if its citizens choose, serve as a laboratory; and may try novel social and economic experiments without risk to the rest of the country.'[4] The same applies, says Professor Gellhorn, to the experiments courageously conducted by a small nation whose traditions and policies are akin to those of the United States. The experiment, he thought, may substantially affect American policy choices for the future.

I will, of course, try to keep some of the differences in mind. They're brought out starkly by the figures mentioned this morning.

The Accident Compensation Scheme: its background and main elements

I come then first to the background to the Accident Compensation Scheme and to its main elements. The history is helpful. Oliver Wendell Holmes, the great American lawyer, began his most notable book *The Common Law* (1880), with the sentence – 'The life of the law has not been logic, it has been experience'. He went on to refer to 'the formative effects of the felt necessities of the time'[5]. He wasn't arguing, of course, that logic was irrelevant. He wasn't arguing that we should be illogical. He wasn't saying either that we should be governed by history. He, indeed, also said that a rule of law was a poor thing if there was no reason for it other than that it had been laid down in the reign of Henry IV. But we cannot, he insisted, know where we are going unless we have a sound idea of where we have been. And I want to try to give you some sense of where we were in the mid 1970s and some sense of where we are going now. And I hope it's a more real sense than that given by the man on the ground who advised Chris James's balloonists that they were simply in the balloon.

Until 1974, those who had been injured had, in general, three remedies under the law of New Zealand. They are essentially those available here at the moment. First, if the injury was at work they could get limited flat-rate compensation which could continue for up to six years if they were still off work and they could get lump-sum payments for permanent physical disability. This scheme, of course, was not dependent on the showing of fault. Second, they could get common law damages if they could show fault by the defendant at work or on the road, at home, in the doctor's surgery, in a hospital, or indeed, anywhere else. I might mention that such evidence as we have indicates that common law actions that were brought for medical negligence were few and far between. Third, somebody who was injured, who couldn't recover under workers' compensation and who couldn't recover for negligence, might be entitled to sickness benefits under the social security scheme if that person met the means test – the income test. There was a statutory criminal injuries scheme. Injured people might also have qualified for sick leave from their employer. They might have had private insurance; and sick leave schemes are a recognition by employers that their responsibility doesn't stop simply with accidents at work. As well, the social security scheme met public hospital costs and certain other medical expenses.

Now, this system was very patchy. It was uneven in its coverage. Financial compensation depended on the lottery of where the injury occurred, whether fault could be proved and the circumstances of the injured person. It was very costly to administer. Twenty-five to 50 per cent of premium income went on administration, legal expenses and other matters – it didn't get into the hands of the person who was injured; it was slow-moving, it impeded rehabilitation. It was also costly to the state because a large number of judges, courtrooms and court staff were tied up in this process.

These arguments are very familiar. They are ones I have read in the debates in the House of Commons on Mrs Barnes's most interesting Bill and the related debate in the House of Lords[6]. It was in the context of mounting criticism in New Zealand that the review was undertaken of the workers' compensation scheme, a review that led, in fact, to a wider and more radical set of proposals.

Perhaps I could elaborate a little on the forces for change. The basic argument was that the system was unjust and that it was inefficient. This was not a satisfactory way of dealing with the problems. As Sir George has just said, a small number of people had windfalls; a large number of people got nothing at all out of the system. So the system then was seen as unfair, unjust, inefficient and moreover (to be fair to the lawyers and thinking of the answer that Chris James gave earlier) there were many lawyers who were engaged in this work who thought it was not professionally satisfying. They actually wanted to move away to work that was more challenging. So there was an element of self-interest, if you like, in the lawyers. Not self-interest in keeping it, but self-interest in moving on to something else. So, in that attitude there is an indication of a relevant social and political philosophy.

The Royal Commission that was set up, chaired by Sir Owen Woodhouse, (a remarkable, very talented New Zealander) recommended a general scheme for immediate compensation for all injured persons without proof of fault, regardless of any fault, and wherever the accident happened[7]. It was based on a number of principles – five of them.

The first was community responsibility. The idea that the whole community had an interest in getting people back on to their feet. Incapacity by injury wasn't just a matter of individual responsibility.

Second, the idea of comprehensive entitlement: that equal losses should be treated equally whatever the cause of the injury.

Third, the idea of complete rehabilitation: that people should be helped to be put back on their feet not just in money terms but in other terms as well. Chris James mentioned the example of his friend whose house was rebuilt to deal with the problems of being a tetraplegic.

Fourth, real compensation. Compensation should not be at some flat-rate means-tested level but should relate in some real way to the previous income level of the person injured.

And finally, administrative efficiency, which obviously must be an important matter. I'll come back to that in the context of the costs of the scheme.

You're already familiar with the main compensation entitlements[8]. Very briefly, they are, first, health and related medical care and, connected with that, rehabilitation services. Second, partial income maintenance during the time off work. That's up to 80 per cent of the individual's earnings in the time before that person was injured. And that, as Chris James mentioned runs up to a maximum figure of NZ$60,000 (£20,000). That's about twice the average wage at the moment. Third, there are elements of lump-sum payments for permanent incapacity and pain and suffering. Those figures have not been subject to increase for some time and they total only NZ$27,000 (£9,000).

So those are the rights: some of them are very valuable. They're supported by levies (if you like by taxes) which are placed on the earners' income (the payroll of the employed and the earnings of the self-employed), on motor vehicle owners and on the general taxpayer. The right to compensation, in other words, has been divorced from the specific liability for any wrongdoing. It is, in general, no longer possible to sue when compensation is available. The Law Commission has recently reviewed the existing compensation scheme[9]. In the course of that time there was a public opinion poll. There were many submissions made to us. There were submissions made at the same time to the Royal Commission on Social Policy[10]. There was the opinion that was being gathered within the Cartwright Enquiry into the National Women's Hospital matter[11] and there is more recent current comment. All of these show that the fundamentals of the scheme are very widely supported in New Zealand. We have not discovered any wish to go back. There are, of course, ideas about improvement: ideas which very often amount to people wanting to pay less and at the same time to have larger benefits. That's part of the process of this sort of review. But the basics have been accepted though there have been continuing calls for change, as I will discuss later. For example, the employers argue that their levies should not extend to non-work accidents and the government is committed to that change. And there is continuing emphasis on professional accountability.

The scheme does, at times, get a bad press. Cases on the margin give an inaccurate impression of what is really going on. I notice that one person in the House of Commons debate in February drew on the case that became very famous in New Zealand of a prisoner either falling or being pushed off the wall of the prison, breaking his legs and arms and getting compensation[12]. Now some people thought that award was pretty outrageous and it is the kind of case that does continue to raise doubts about the scheme in people's minds. But basically there is extremely wide support for the scheme and that support is based on its 24-hour coverage for the consequences of all injury, on the speed of the process and on its efficiency. Decisions are taken within short periods. There are delays sometimes on lump-sum payments but for earnings-related payments, for medical benefits and rehabilitation, decisions are made promptly and payments are made within days.

It is a fact that costs of the scheme have been increasing in a worrying way recently. That matter has been examined by a number of bodies including the Law Commission[13]. But they've got to be put into perspective. Let me mention a couple of figures, one of them because it was mentioned in the House of Commons debate. The basic daily cost for each New Zealander for this 24-hour coverage is about one dollar (35p). That's the figure at the level of the individual citizen. In 1987 the cost to the country was about 1.2 per cent of Gross Domestic Product (GDP)[14]. I see that a publication of the Royal College of Physicians says 1.4 per cent[15]. That may be a more accurate recent figure. That figure was referred to in the debate in the House of Commons as showing our scheme was very costly. Now that figure by itself means little: it's got to be compared with something. Incidentally it is the figure for the whole scheme and not simply for the medical malpractice part as a former Junior Health Minister (Mrs Edwina Currie) thought in the debate[16]. We compared the 1.2 per cent figure with the Australian combined figure for third party motor vehicle insurance and employers' liability insurance. We thought that if we were to compare our comprehensive levy payments, with that combined figure we would get an interesting answer. The Australian figure was 1.7 per cent when we did this comparison. And of course, that 1.7 per cent of GDP does not cover non-work or non-road accidents. It does not cover medical malpractice. It does not cover the cost of government payments because governments in Australia, as elsewhere, are self-employed. So on the face of it, our scheme is a cheap one. That also appears from another comparison, that between the levies which are paid by particular employers. Our scheme is on the whole cheaper than the workers' compensation schemes in New South Wales, British Columbia or Ontario – and those schemes provide narrower coverage.

I think it's important to try to get some of these facts clearly in the public domain to remove some of the mischief that is sometimes spoken about these schemes. It's not possible to make a relevant comparison with the United Kingdom because, at least according to the debate on the Bill in February, there are no comparative figures that can be drawn on.

We have then a very widely supported scheme. A scheme based on sound principle, but a scheme that is subject to review right at this moment and subject to the prospect of major change.

The scheme in practice: medical misadventure

I now come to my second heading: how does this scheme operate in practice, especially in the area of medical misadventure? What are the problems of causation and natural causes and what about costs? The medical cases need to be put in context. The total number of new claims notified to the Accident Compensation Corporation (ACC) in recent years is about 170,000 claims a year. That's up somewhat from earlier years but the figures are not exactly comparable. What has gone up is the length of time that individuals are staying on earnings-related compensation, leading to a serious concern about the money that is being spent on the scheme. In part, that results from legislative change[17], but in part it is a mark of a sad feature of present-day New Zealand, growing unemployment. People, in some cases, are continuing to receive compensation because they can't find jobs to return to. Part of the increase though, arises from its maturing – the scheme is now 17 years old. There are now a larger number of people in the scheme who are there on a fairly long-term or permanent basis[18]. That aspect of the increased cost should have been anticipated.

It's not clear, as I indicated in an answer that I gave this morning, how many of these claims are for medical misadventure. The ACC has some good statistics, but in this area, I'm afraid, the statistics are not as good as they might be. Steps are now being taken to get better figures, and there is an associated trial scheme for the handling of medical misadventure claims.

The area of medical misadventure has not been one of major concern within the ACC, but I should note, first of all, that there is now considerable controversy about some medical claims, in particular those arising out of the National Women's Hospital research that has been mentioned already today. And second, there is a partly consequential increase in the number of disputes about medical coverage in the Accident Compensation Appeal Authority and in the courts.

Before I come to the question of just what is covered by the scheme in the medical misadventure area, I could mention the position of individual doctors under it. They pay, or the employers pay, levies to the ACC. The payment is a little over one dollar per hundred dollars of earnings. And they are entitled to the compensation and benefits that I mentioned earlier, if they are injured by accident at work or anywhere else. So they have benefits under the scheme at a modest price. And of course, on the other side, they're not in general subject to civil suit. There is immunity from legal action if there is coverage under the Act. That means that the indemnity payments that they make to the medical defence organisations are modest. And indeed, they are mainly made up, as I understand it, of contributions towards the medical disciplinary processes – the matters that we were talking about this morning. Some part of the payment is for civil suit because in limited circumstances it is possible for actions to be brought. To answer a question that was put this morning, one set of figures that I have from one of the medical defence organisations is that in five years there were about 30 medical negligence cases brought. Only one of them went to trial. And there are, of course, cases that are before the court now arising from the National Women's matter. So civil cases continue to come to court but in very limited numbers.

What then is meant by 'personal injury by accident'? And what is meant by 'medical misadventure' which is an element of the definition of personal injury by accident. These are the two statutory terms[19]. As Chris James mentioned, the scope of coverage has been broadened by interpretation over the years of the scheme. That means both a wider entitlement to those injured and a wider immunity from suit for the health professionals and services.

At first there was considerable caution. I quote from a judgement given in the High Court in 1980:

'All treatments, whether medical or surgical, have a chance of being unsuccessful. There is an expected failure rate in all of these matters and such failure may be because no matter how correct the treatment, nature does not always respond in the desired way. It would be quite beyond the intention or wording of the Accident Compensation Act that cover should be granted on the basis of personal injury by accident merely because the medical treatment was not a 100 per cent effective. Certainty cannot be underwritten.'[20]

The judge went on 'The word misadventure is defined in some dictionaries as being ill-luck or bad fortune. It would seem that this wording has been introduced into the Act to cover a wider variety of accidental occurrences than merely the consequence of medical negligence.' To interpolate, the scheme does give wider cover than the previous law. The judge continued:

'It is in the nature of medical and surgical treatment that unexpected and abnormal consequences may follow to a greater or lesser degree depending upon the simplicity or sophistication of the treatment being undertaken. Where

74

there is an unsatisfactory outcome of treatment which can be classified as merely within the normal range of medical or surgical failure attendant upon the most felicitous treatment, it could not be held to be misadventure.'

So while there did not have to be negligence there had to be some element then of ill-luck, of bad fortune, of real misadventure; the fact that the result was reasonably predictable was not sufficient. There had to be something unexpected, something undesigned. There had to be unlikelihood, an element emphasising the patient's point of view and indicating to the doctor the possible relevance of informed consent.

One judicial elaboration given in 1985 included the following illustrations of cases which would come within the meaning of misadventure:

If the risk of an adverse consequence is considered slight but nevertheless the patient suffers that adverse consequence, it can be said that such an unlikely occurrence is injury by misadventure as having the factor of mischance or bad fortune.

If the risk of some minor adverse consequence is likely but in the event the consequence proves to be grave, it can be said that such a grave consequence is injury by misadventure for the same reason.

An adverse consequence not foreseen at all would clearly be injury for the same reason.

An adverse consequence from a known risk which might well have been avoided, had certain damage been detected (without negligence or medical error) could also be injury by misadventure, as the patient is either the worse for some mishap or has been the victim of 'a piece of bad fortune'[21].

The 1989 judgement of the Court of Appeal in the National Women's case, *Green v Matheson*[22], appears to have taken the matter further. One of the women who had been the subject of the programme of treatment at the National Women's Hospital sued the doctor mainly responsible for the treatment; his superior, the Medical Superintendent of the hospital; the teaching University and the Hospital Board, for trespass to the person, breach of fiduciary duty, and negligence. The Court of Appeal held that no claim could be brought in respect of those matter arising after 1 April 1974 (the beginning date of ACC), except for exemplary damages. They were claims arising from personal injury by accident and medical misadventure and were covered by the Act. For the Court of Appeal, personal injury by accident in its natural and ordinary sense is well capable of applying to any adverse consequences to a patient's health caused by wrong medical treatment. It had the same view of 'medical misadventure' on the facts of this case: if the plaintiff's case were mishandled 'it was her misfortune or ill-luck'. And all the consequences for which she had sued were physical or mental consequences within the meaning of the Act. The elements of the unexpected and the unintended appear to have been given less significance.

The tests in the case are ones that potentially could involve very long and complex litigation but that doesn't seem to have happened yet. It is possible to envisage the assembly of complex statistical material about the real amount of risk and difficult judgements about likelihood. Consider, for example, the side-effects of drugs, the chance of IUDs becoming embedded or wandering, or to mention the case that was decided just last week, an unexpected – as they all are of course – an unexpected cot death where the Appeal Authority has held that the particular cot death in question was medical misadventure[23].

All of these cases, I think, illustrate a more basic worry in many New Zealanders' minds and it is this: why should the fact that the mishap has a known risk, and that there is informed consent to it, be relevant to cover? After all, we all know that there is a risk in driving on the roads and yet no-one would say that if we are injured on the roads we are not entitled to accident compensation cover. So there is then behind this movement towards a somewhat wider definition a basic policy problem.

But there are still areas of medical malpractice which are not covered. For example, a simple negligent failure to answer a call or to make a medical intervention might still be actionable. There was at least one such successful action in the early years of the scheme and actions can still be brought for exemplary damages[24]. But for the most part there is a wide coverage and a wide correlative immunity. The law does however involve a difficult line which produces uncertainty, contention and litigation. There are a significant number of recent reported decisions[25]. But I should keep this in perspective. The ACC gives as many as 170,000 answers a year to claims. It makes that many decisions. Only about 1:500 of those cases goes to the Appeal Authority and under half of those are decided in favour of the claimant. The very large proportion of cases are decided at the level of the ACC without further controversy[26].

While there are some concerns in the medical misadventure area and some increase in them in recent years there has been no major controversy or major difficulty. In particular we haven't had a substantial problem yet about causation. This appears, for example, from Walter Gellhorn's article and from papers which Margaret McGregor Vennell, a very able tort lawyer who is also a member of the Accident Compensation Corporation Board, has given[27]. Their writings and the recently reported decisions of the Authority do not show major difficulties in that area. Now, it may be that we have been fortunate so far. It may be, for example, that the growing number of cases relating to asbestos-related diseases will bring a change, though in that area the problems are reduced by the fact that it is not usually necessary to attribute the cause for such a disease to one particular employment. The problem has not reared its head to the extent that some anticipated at the outset[28].

The principal concern expressed in this area related to the anomaly in this scheme, as in many others, of drawing a line between incapacity caused by injury and incapacity caused by illness. There is also, to repeat, concern (to think about the dicussion this morning) about the methods for ensuring compliance with good professional standards. I now turn to some of the proposals which have been made to try to remove some of the difficulties which I've mentioned.

Proposals for change

There is the sense of paradox, I suppose, in the fact that we do keep having reviews and we do keep having these proposals for change. Outside observers, when they come and look at our scheme, tend to confirm the general opinion which I mentioned earlier about the great value of the scheme. They, of course, sometimes suggest improvements. I think that there are two main reasons for this review process. The first involves problems relating to the scheme itself because there are some difficulties within it, including that of its increasing cost. Those difficulties have arisen partly from capricious decisions taken by successive governments first, to cut levies paid by employers, second, to increase them greatly and more recently, to cut them again. So there's been a roller-coaster of money coming in to earners' fund. Second, there have been continuing attempts to address the anomaly of the illness/injury line. And looking beyond the scheme, we have had attempts in New Zealand to review and reform the whole of our welfare arrangements.

We live in quite remarkable times in terms of the willingness of successive New Zealand governments to look in a basic way at large parts of our economic, social, welfare, health and educational systems; at times those systems seem to be in a state of continuous as well as courageous experimentation, to go back to that adjective. Some people start to think that there should be a moratorium on some of these movements. Certainly, there is a danger of burn-out at the level of the people who have to try to handle them.

Let me just say a word or two about the proposals for change. Some relate to the problem of definition of medical misadventure. That problem can be handled in a variety of ways. First, it can be left to the courts. We have noted the problem that causes.

Second the consequence of the distinction could be reduced. Some health benefits, for example, are paid differentially according to whether there is an injury or an illness. The figures show that if we were to put all of those health benefit payments together it is possible to treat the ill and the injured on an equal footing. This could be so, for example, in respect of visits to the doctor, specialist treatments, drugs, X-rays and lab tests. It isn't necessary to maintain the difference that we have between illness and injury in that respect. All that is required, it appeared to the Law Commission when we examined this, was political will to apply the money evenly across the board. It was not a matter of bringing in more money, it was a matter of applying it more evenly and more fairly. Not only would the system be fairer, it would be administratively cheaper and it would prevent petty fraud by doctors and their patients. The payments made by the state would have to be at an adequate level.

If lump-sum payments were no longer part of the scheme (for they are anomalous in this kind of scheme), and if they were replaced by a different type of periodic payment for those who are seriously and permanently disabled (whether by illness or injury), then a further part of the significance of the illness/injury line would disappear.

A third approach to the difficulties of definition would be to abandon 'medical misadventure' as the test and to use the World Health Organisation's (WHO) international classification of diseases. That classification does provide a way of getting a clearer definition of what is to be covered and what is to be excluded. The line could be adjusted as appropriate and that would relieve much administrative doubt and worry. The Law Commission proposed that[29].

The fourth and most dramatic step of all would be to extend the scheme as a whole to incapacity caused by illness and thereby so far as possible remove the current distinction. The distinction has been regarded from the outset as contrary to principle. Let me just quote from what Sir Owen Woodhouse and his colleagues had to say back in 1967 about the fact that they were going to recommend compensation for all those who were injured and not cover those who were incapacitated by illness. They said:

'It may ask how incapacity arising from sickness and disease can be left aside. In logic there is no answer. A man overcome by ill-health is no more able to work and no less afflicted than his neighbour hit by a car. In the industrial field certain diseases are included already. But logic on this occasion must give way to other considerations. First, it might be thought unwise to attempt one massive leap when two considered steps can be taken. Second, the urgent need is to co-ordinate the unrelated systems at present working in the injury field. Third, there is a virtual absence of the statistical signposting which alone can demonstrate the feasibility of the further move. And finally, the proposals now put forward for

79

injury leave the way entirely open for sickness to follow whenever the relevant decision is taken.'[30]

Both the previous government and the present agree in principle that the scheme should be extended. In 1989 the statistical work to which Sir Owen and his colleagues referred was undertaken. Late last year, the Labour government introduced a Bill which provided for that extension[31]. The new government established a working party to prepare proposals on that footing[32]. These proposals have given rise to controversy and to large questions about the scope of the scheme and its funding on which I wish to make two comments.

The comment on funding is that when work was done in 1989 on a possible extension, it was found that the essence of the present injury scheme could be extended within the current funds that were then available. That was a surprising conclusion. Certainly surprising to me. One of the reasons that extension was possible 'within current overall financial bounds', the expression which the Minister of Finance used in the budget that year, was that the earners' levy at that time was high, higher than it is now – though, as I have indicated, not that high compared with comparable workers' compensation rates elsewhere. Reserves had been built up, there were tax implications in the changes that were being proposed and there was to be brought into the calculation money that was currently being spent under the social security scheme for invalids and sickness benefits. So the government was able to say in 1989, and subsequent developments have built on this, that extension looked feasible. But there is an open question about that now. Our economy is not as healthy as we thought it was then and there are questions about just what money is available. There are also serious questions about the detail of the scheme.

My comment on the scope of the scheme relates to proposals which were floated earlier this year by one senior minister about the fragmentation of the scheme. I mentioned earlier the argument by the employers that they should not have to pay for non-work accidents. That has led to suggestions that the scheme might be divided up; we might get a road accident scheme and a work accident scheme, and then there would be a third scheme which, on one view, would be the subject of first party insurance. This is a frightening thing to contemplate. At first public attention was given to sporting injuries and, as you might expect, to rugby injuries because it's always easy to add up those figures and show some footage of people trampling on one another and raise the question – why on earth should the general scheme pay for them? There was a growing worry about home accidents. And I imagine in many people's minds there was a growing concern about medical malpractice because the argument was starting to be heard, well if we're no longer going to be covered by a universal scheme in accordance with the general 'social contract' (that was reached back in 1974), shouldn't we be allowed to sue? The jury is still out on all of that though the government insists that the scheme must have regard to the abolition of the right to sue. But I think the points are being pressed very vigorously on ministers that some of these proposed changes, as well as being contrary to principle, do not save money. They increase administrative costs, they increase the delays in payment, they impede rehabilitation. And also, so far at least, the insurance companies appear to be showing no real interest in them.

I'd like to conclude just by making three points. The first is that there are problems at the margin of the scheme so far as medical misadventure is concerned. As I've indicated there may be an increase in the number of cases which test that margin. There are, however, ways of handling that margin and there is perhaps the prospect of completion of the scheme in the way that was envisaged back in 1967.

Second, notwithstanding the difficulties the scheme has faced from time to time, it is broadly accepted. It is seen as being in accordance with principle. It is seen, when people examine the figures, as being a cheap and effective way of handling many of the problems that arise. It would be very sad, I think, if we were to see the beginnings of a dismantling of it. Some North Americans who are expert in these areas have talked to the working party looking at these matters. They emphasised to that working party the value again, as seen by outsiders, of the scheme and one of them at least urged the working party to leave well alone[33].

My conclusion, going back to the dual themes of the conference, relates to the importance as I see it of treating compensation issues separately from accountability ones. On that I'm preaching to the converted. It is, of course, the view that was expressed by the English barrister I mentioned at the outset, in that article nearly 100 years ago. The Law Commission gave a good deal of attention to the question of accountability in our review of the scheme because, as I said, it was a matter that was pressed on us in various contexts. We were told that we should use the levy system to provide incentives to better behaviour. We found, and we asked for argument and materials, that there was absolutely no evidence at all that the levy system would affect the behaviour of the people who were subject to it. They were going to behave fairly and sensibly and reasonably as employers, or as drivers, or as doctors or whatever, for all kinds of other reasons quite independently of the accident scheme. And I think that does go back to the matters that we were talking about this morning, to the great importance of seeing to it that the accountability regime is enhanced and improved[34]. Chris James mentioned some of the possible changes that are being examined. Some of the accountability mechanisms are of course at work right at the moment. You're probably tired of hearing of the Cartwright Enquiry, but it seems to me that that one Enquiry had much more impact on the general attitude of the medical profession and on the people who deal with them than all the tort cases we have ever had in New Zealand. That is a much more effective way, even after the event, of calling people to account for their wrongdoings. Education, obviously, is important in that. The disciplinary processes which are still being developed are important. The work of ethics committees is important and so on. There is a great range of ways in which we can try to improve the system of accountability, the standards of the profession; not just the medical profession but others as well. Much better ways it seems to me than through the compensation scheme.

It is critical that we should try to get principled and efficient compensation schemes which are aimed at rehabilitation and at meeting the other economic problems of those who are seriously incapacitated. Those schemes should be developed essentially independently of the accountability regimes which also are very important. Thank you very much, Mr Chairman.

Subsequent developments

The above paper refers to a review of the Accident Compensation Scheme which the newly elected government announced in December 1990. In its first budget, delivered on 30 July 1991, the government announced its policy decisions based on the review. According to the Minister responsible for 'one of the world's most advanced schemes for compensating the victims of accidents', the scheme is showing signs of stress:

'It is no longer seen as being fair, there is significant level of abuse, and the costs of the scheme are not shared equitably'.

The Minister then mentioned the preferred treatment of victims of accident compared with victims of sickness; the 'dramatic' increases in the cost of the scheme and the fact that last year employers' contributions covered nearly 70 per cent of all payments though less than 40 per cent of payments were for work accidents. According to the Minister:

'The government is committed to reforming the scheme in ways that make it both fair and affordable, and to correcting inequalities in the scheme without reintroducing the right to sue for personal injury'.

The particular decisions include the following:

Funding

- employers' premiums will not cover non-work accidents
- employers will meet the public health costs of work injuries
- earners will pay a premium to meet the cost of their non-work injuries
- motorists will meet the public health costs of motor vehicle injuries
- motor vehicle costs will be met not just from the owners' premium but also from a petrol tax and if possible from drivers' premiums

83

- experience rating will be applied to employers and possibly to earners and motor vehicle owners.

Entitlements

- injury conditions will be more clearly defined
- consideration is to be given to disqualifications for unacceptable behaviour
- earnings related compensation will continue on the same terms as at present
- however that compensation will not be provided after 12 months where the capacity to work exceeds 85 per cent; unemployment benefit becomes the appropriate income support for a person who cannot find work
- lump sums for loss of faculty and for pain, suffering and loss of enjoyment of life will be replaced by a disability allowance of up to NZ$40 a week for loss of faculty, with a 15 per cent incapacity threshold
- an integrated regime of user part charges for health care for illness and injury will be introduced.

Other matters

- legislation will be introduced to effect changes in medical disciplinary procedures and, when appropriate, other health professions
- the scheme will be administered in the meantime by the ACC as the sole insurer
- the ACC and other agencies involved are to recognise the need to avoid duplication of effect in the field of accident prevention.

See Honourable W F Birch, *Accident Compensation: A Fairer Scheme* 30 July 1991. See also the Report (March 1991) and First Supplementary Report (26 April 1991) of the Ministerial Working Party on Accident Compensation and Incapacity (released in August 1991).

Except for the change to petrol tax which was introduced and enacted in the Budget legislation, the remaining decisions (some of which remain to be taken and to be refined) are still to be the subject of Bills and of parliamentary consideration. The changes to the benefits are scheduled to take effect on 1 July 1992.

References

1. House of Commons Debates, Hansard for 1 February 1991 cols 1223–1292.
2. W Gorst Clay, 'The Law of Employers' Liability and Insurance against Accidents' (1987) 2 *Journal of the Society of Comparative Legislation* 1, 1–2.
3. 'Medical Malpractice Litigation (US) – Medical Mishap Compensation (NZ)' (1988) 73 Cornell L Rev 170. The Ombudsman article, 'The Ombudsman in New Zealand' (1965) 53 *Calif L Rev* 1155 was also published in *Ombudsmen and Others* (1966) ch 3.
4. The original statement was made by Justice Brandeis in *New State Ice Co v Liebman* (1932) 285 US 262, 311.
5. *The Common Law* (181) 1.
6. See note 1 above and the House of Lords Debates, Hansard for 20 February 1991 columns 553 – 586.
7. *Report of the Royal Commission on Compensation for Personal Injury in New Zealand* (1967). For discussions see Palmer, *Compensation for Incapacity: a study of law and social change in New Zealand and Australia* (1979) and Ison, *Accident Compensation; a commentary on the New Zealand Scheme* (1980), and in the present context Sir Owen Woodhouse, 'The New Zealand Experience' in Halley and others (eds), *Medical Malpractice Solutions; Systems and Proposals for Injury Compensation* (1989) 171.
8. See the Accident Compensation Act 1982.
9. *The Accident Compensation Scheme (Interim Report on Aspects of Funding)* (1987 NZLR R3), and *Personal Injury: Prevention and Recovery (Report on the Accident Compensation Scheme)* (1988 NZLC R4). The writer also convened an interdepartmental working party which reported in 1989 on the extension of the scheme to incapacity caused by sickness.
10. *Report of the Royal Commission on Social Policy* (April 1988), vol III, part Two, *Future Directions 569–613*.
11. *Report of the Cervical Cancer Inquiry 1988*.
12. Mrs Barnes MP note 1 above, column 1229.
13. *Personal Injury*, note 9 above, paras 83–102 and appendix c; see also the Index under Cost and Expenditure.
14. *Ibid*, para 16.
15. Report of the Royal College of Physicians, *Compensation for Adverse Consequences of Medical Intervention* (December 1990) para 5.29.

16. Note 1, column 1256. Mr Frank Doran MP promptly pointed out her error, column 1257.
17. Accident Compensation Act 1982 s 59(2) as amended in 1985.
18. See eg Personal Injury, note 9 above, paras 86–89.
19. Accident Compensation Act 1982 s 2(1):
    'Personal injury by accident' -
    (a) Includes -
        (i) The physical and mental consequences of any such injury or of the accident:
        (ii) Medical, surgical, dental, or first aid misadventure:
    (b) Except as provided in the last preceding paragraph, does not include -
        (i) Damage to the body or mind caused by a cardio-vascular or cerebro-vascular episode unless the episode is the result of effort, strain, or stress that is abnormal, excessive, or unusual for the person suffering it, and the effort, strain or stress arises out of and in the course of the employment of that person:
        (ii) Damage to the body or mind caused exclusively by disease, infection, or the aging process:
20. *ACC v Auckland Hospital Board* [1980] 2 NZLR 748, 751.
21. *MacDonald v ACC* [1985] 5 NZAR 276, 281 (HC).
22. *Green v Matheson* [1989] 3 NZLR 564 CA.
23. *Philpott v ACC* [1991] NZAR 331.
24. *Donselaar v Donselaar* [1982] 1 NZLR 97 CA.
25. For recent cases see eg *Viggars v ACC* (1986) 6 NZAR 235, *Polansky v ACC* [1990] NZAR 481, *Mitchell v ACC* [1991] NZAR 105 and see the discussions in Gellhorn, note 3 above the Vennell note 27 below.
26. See the annual reports of the Corporation, eg 1989 pp 16–17.
27. McGregor Vennell, 'Medical Misfortune in a No Fault Society' in Mann and Havard (eds) *No Fault Compensation in Medicine* (1989) 33.
28. Eg Epstein cited by Gellhorn note 3, 193 n 66.
29. Personal Injury, note 9 above, paras 8, 165, 281 and draft Safety, Rehabilitation and Compensation Act (p 104) s 12 and first schedule.
30. Report note 7 above, para 17.
31. Incapacity and Rehabilitation Bill 1990.
32. The reports of that working party have been released since this paper was delivered. They show, unfortunately, that the working party did not consider the question of the extension of the scheme to incapacity caused by sickness. See the note at the end of the paper.
33. See Craig Brown and John Smillie 'The Future of Accident Compensation' July 1991 *New Zealand Law Journal*.
34. *Personal Injury*, note 9 above, paras 105–149. See also the valuable demonstrations by an outstanding New Zealand scholar of the ineffectiveness of the law of torts as a deterrent – and its

poor performance on the compensation side as well, Donald Harris, Director of the Centre for Socio-Legal Studies, Oxford, 'Can the law of Torts Fulfil its Aims?' (1990) 14 *NZULR* 113, and 'Tort Law Reform in the United States' (1991) 11 *OJLS* 407.

Dr Barry Manuel

What may happen if there is no change in the UK system?

Dr Barry Manuel

Associate Dean, Professor of Surgery Boston University School of Medicine, President, Massachusetts Medical Society, and Contributor to the New England Journal of Medicine

I shall attempt this afternoon to share with you what happens in a country (USA) which uses the tort system to adjudicate its professional liability claims. A country which pays its attorneys on a contingency basis. A country with one of the world's highest densities of attorneys – attorneys whose ability to expand the doctrine of causation and whose creativity in creating mischief knows no limits.

In due deference to the location of this conference, I shall keep it R-rated rather than X-rated.

In the United States we had our first crisis in professional liability in the mid '70s. What I would like to do today is spend just a bit of time telling you about that and about the response of government to that crisis. I shall explain why that response proved inadequate and why the inadequacy of that response has had a major negative effect on the quality of our health care.

In the early '70s the insurance company actuaries actually fell asleep and didn't recognise that there was an increase in frequency of claims and severity of awards in medical malpractice. When they discovered what was going on, they took, in our country – the usual option – they just discontinued the line, and we went from 39 companies offering medical malpractice insurance to eight. And those eight that remained in the field charged premiums which for many physicians were unaffordable. At that time all 50 states passed legislation. Over 300 statutes were enacted. We were indeed in crisis.

I want to share with you some of the common responses of the states to the crisis. Joint underwriting associations (JUA) were established which guaranteed availability of professional liability insurance. This was one of the most important things because we could not otherwise obtain insurance. Thirty-five states established this kind of company which provided immediate insurance availability and indeed most of the JUAs remain an option today, though not very frequently used. We established screening panels. We eliminated the addendum clause (I don't know if you have it here); that's when a specific amount is claimed in the damages. We had reduction in the statute of limitation. We had capping of physician's liability. We had an attempt at limitation of lawyer's fees. We had the establishment of commissions to study the medical liability problem. There was really no data on the problem until that time. We had generic improvements in the tort laws. We had the beginning of Physician Mutuals, and that was another effort at providing insurance: a most successful effort. Since the mid '70s, Physician Mutuals have increased the number of covered doctors every year to the present where they insure over 60 per cent of physicians in the United States. We had the establishment of a collateral source rules.

Now, what happened with all these legislative changes? To illustrate what's happened with severity of awards: figure 1 shows the average medical malpractice verdict in the United States at this time. Since 1980 there were some peaks and valleys. At the present time the average medical malpractice verdict is just under $1.2 million, and in our country most physicians cannot purchase more than $1 million in coverage. In figure 2 the aggregate professional liability premiums paid by physicians in the past ten years are the bars, and as you can see, they have continued to

What may happen if there is no change in the UK system?

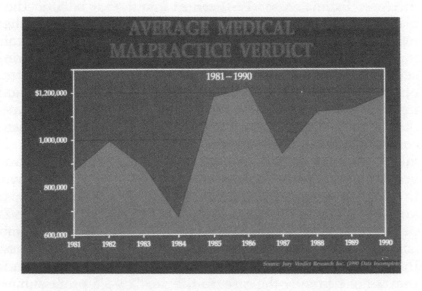

Figure 1

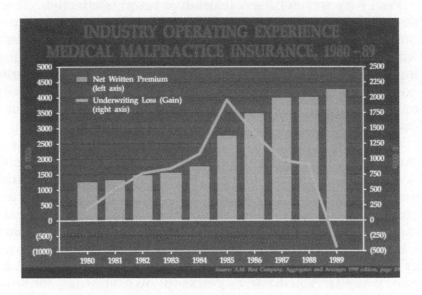

Figure 2

increase. Estimates for 1990 are at about $5.5 billion. The black line just talks about insurance company losses. This has not been a very attractive product for the medical malpractice carriers, showing losses every year as you can see. These are all losses, and these are true losses after off-set of investment income. There are a lot of things insurance companies do in our country. For a long time we didn't understand. We kept being told that the insurance companies were losing a great deal of money. They would take premiums of $100 in 1980. By the time the claim had gone through the tort system, they'd paid out $150, let's say, in 1990. They would claim to have lost 50 per cent on this kind of coverage. What they didn't tell us is that they earn 7 per cent a year on our premiums and so by 1990 they actually had approximately $200 and made 50 per cent on this coverage. But we've become more sophisticated and that is not currently the case. In the year 1985/6 professional liability insurers did lose over $2 billion. They have since become barely profitable. We're not quite sure what is happening at this time, but we're beginning to see an increase in frequency of claims. This followed a slight decrease in frequency which has occurred in the United States in the last 18 months.

Well why weren't these legislative reforms effective? The so-called tribunals have really been rendered unconstitutional in most states. Through a variety of legal manoeuvres tribunals have been emasculated as a mechanism for ferreting out claims in other states. A larger number of claims are going to court. The lawyers have discovered the fertile field of birth defects. That's already been alluded to, and I shall do so again. Punitive damages are being assessed.

In our country, let me tell you how that works. First of all, punitive damages are awarded when there's gross negligence versus ordinary negligence, and that is left up to a lay jury to decide. The way it now works in our country is that you get notification that you're being sued for medical malpractice and promptly go into a state of shock. Your insurance carrier usually comes in and tries to assuage some of the anxiety, and after that's done, before he leaves, he tells you that you have to get your own attorney for the punitive damages because those are criminal charges and insurance doesn't cover them. And then you really stew for a while until your friendly plaintiff attorney calls you and says 'You know, doctor, I hated to ask for punitive damages but my client really wanted me to do that. However, if you get your insurance company to settle the case, I'll drop the punitive damages.' Now, it's one thing if you feel that this may have been a maloccurrence and there was not any malpractice, and you want to fight the charges knowing that you have the full faith of a large insurance company behind you. It's quite another one when you're out there on a limb alone with your total personal assets at risk. The use of punitive damages has been a very successful tool in the hands of our attorneys.

Change in the statute of limitation. Most states in the United States now define the statute as beginning at the time of discovery, and they define discovery as the time when someone informs you that there may have been malpractice. What that essentially does is eliminate any statute of limitations. We, at one time, had a flurry of interest in counter-suits by physicians particularly for nuisance claims. While the lower courts were very good to us, the superior courts all overruled any verdict in favour of the physician. The Supreme Court has not heard any appeals, indicating to me at least, that our court system is saying that an attorney's only responsibility is to his client.

Increased publicity over large settlements – I think that's obvious but I will show you something that we live with in just a moment.

Attorneys have become much more sophisticated. There is a neurosurgeon who's become a plaintiff's attorney and sits with a reservoir of over 200 'bad baby' cases awaiting trial. There are many people of that nature.

I mentioned to you the creativity of our legal bar. Hedonistic damages are something new. We have a lot of general damages in our country, such things as pain and suffering, loss of consortium. Now we have loss of enjoyment of life. We currently have 17 states allowing hedonistic damages which compound on top of the specific damages and other general damages I mentioned.

And then we have awards associated with AIDS – contaminated blood transfusions, and that's something that is frightening all of us. At the present time we have just one case of AIDS secondary to a blood transfusion that has wound its way through the appeals process of our courts[1]. A case of a neonatologist who transfused a child at birth one unit of blood. Everybody agrees the indications were solid, and it was done before there was any test for the AIDS virus, in early 1985. The child developed AIDS. A lay jury awarded $28.7 million for that case. It was appealed and, under the appeals process there was a settlement of $6.5 million[2]. And that's how juries in our country value such occurrences.

We estimate that there were 30,000 units of blood transfused between 1980/5 before a commercial test became available to identify HIV virus. At the present time there are over 300 AIDS suits secondary to transfusion pending in the USA. I think it portends very poorly for the future. And contrast that, if you will, with the rest of the world. Germany just settled a large number of cases of AIDS-related transfusions in haemophiliacs. They did so with an average total reimbursement of US$50,000. I was just reading in *The Times* on the way over here yesterday, that your government has done the same thing at an average, if my maths is correct, of $16,000 per claim. Contrast that with the one case which, in our country, almost always creates a floor for damages, and subsequently awards usually go above that floor. So, AIDS does portend poorly for the future in the case of professional liability.

Then we have so-called professional plaintiff's physicians, an exceedingly noxious group of individuals. I've been interested in professional liability for a number of years, and 20 years ago you would see some physicians testify out of their specialty (perhaps a clinical instructor in pulmonary medicine testifying in a complicated thoracic aneurysm case) clearly using a medical school title, albeit minor, to create some credibility. What we see now is some of our most distinguished professors in the United States who are testifying for plaintiff's attorneys not once, not twice, but 10/20/ 36 times a year. And there is nothing we can do about it. They travel the United States using this activity to supplement their income. We write about it, but try as we may, our hands are bound. We can't do anything to stop this activity.

How would you like to wake up in the morning, pick up your paper and see your friendly attorney with a full-page advertisement in the paper asking 'What should you do when you think you're the victim of medical malpractice?'.

In these ads there's some talk about how they specialise in 'back' cases and 'bad baby' cases. In another advertisement seen on television there is a classroom where everyone is attending except one child who is always looking out the window, and they say 'If your child has a learning disability, it could have been caused by malpractice during the birthing process, call your friendly attorney'. This is seen on the television, it is in the newspaper and it's on the radio. This is what we have to deal with all the time.

In our opinion, professional liability doesn't really belong in a courtroom at all. The physician is not tried by a jury of his peers. I challenge any physician in the United States to obtain a jury of his peers, a true jury of his peers. Juries tend to be emotionally very sensitive to injured patients, and that makes for very large awards as in the AIDS case. It is very difficult sometimes, even for professionals to decide between the fine line of professional liability and maloccurrence. And you can imagine the problems that a lay jury has?

Due to prolonged litigation, the truly injured patient does have to wait an inordinate amount of time to receive any compensation. It takes about two years from the time of a medical maloccurrence until the suit is filed. To go through the busy jurisdictions of our court system can take five to seven years. So it's a long time before someone who is truly injured receives any payment.

There are several areas that I really want to emphasise. This is one. Our present system causes great injury to the physician, his family and reputation, and rarely is that damage reversible, even if the physician is exonerated by the courts. And then of course there is the cost of our system. At the present time the overhead costs of our system account for 75 per cent of the physician's premium with only 25 per cent going to the patient: a grossly inefficient system.

Sarah Charles is an academic psychiatrist at the University of Illinois. Following two years of defending herself from a medical negligence suit, she did an extensive survey of doctors who were sued for medical malpractice[3]. Although we knew there was a great deal of emotional trauma associated with a malpractice suit, this really surprised us. Thirty-nine per cent of physicians admitted to four or five symptoms suggestive of a major depression; 20 per cent acknowledged another group of symptoms including anger, change of mood, tension, frustration and the like; 8 per cent noted the onset of physical illness, of which 2 per cent had a myocardial infarction; 8 per cent noted the aggravation of a previously diagnosed illness; 18.8 per cent felt a loss of nerve in a clinical situation; 14 per cent felt less self-confident. I call your attention to the next figure: 56.5 per cent said they and their families had suffered as a result of the suit. These findings have been replicated by a number of studies since that time, except one finding. Sixty per cent of insured doctors are insured by Physician Mutuals, they did a survey of spouses of physicians who had been sued. They found that 100 per cent of spouses felt their families had been severely affected by the suit; 19 per cent felt that their practices had suffered; 33.6 per cent contemplated retirement. This degree of emotional damage is unacceptable but the worst part is that 75 per cent of the physicians experiencing this emotional trauma were later acquitted by the courts. So it is the litigation process which is so very damaging to physicians.

The other area that I do wish to emphasise on which professional liability has had a very major effect is on three critical components of health care: access, quality and cost. The Institute of Medicine is a division of the National Academy of Sciences in the United States, independent and highly prestigious. They did an extensive study of obstetric care which was published in the *New England Journal of Medicine*[4]. They concluded that obstetric care in the United States is being severely affected by our method of dealing with professional liability, particularly to economically-disadvantaged women. And they said, parenthetically, it is destroying the doctor/patient relationship. I would submit to you that similar studies done on any high-risk specialty, such as neurosurgery, orthopaedics and now emergency room medicine would yield exactly the same results.

At a University Commemorative Day Ceremony at Johns Hopkins University on 22 February 1990, we were all amazed that our President called attention to this problem and he said in his speech:

'...We've to remember a simple truth: not every unfortunate medical outcome is the result of poor medicine.

96

You cannot make life risk-free. No risk means no progress. And that's not the American way. I also worry that the fear of malpractice limits the access to many Americans in our rural areas to quality medical care – particularly those with high-risk cases. Clearly, we must find a fair and reasonable solution to the medical malpractice crisis'.

Now to the issue of quality of health care. There are many examples. When Vincent DeVita was President of the American Cancer Society he created quite a stir when he estimated that the number of cancer victims who die as a result of less than optimal treatment (under-treatment), may number 10,000 or more annually. 'Malpractice is behind it in part. Doctors are frightened to death of malpractice'. At the same conference, Dr William Hryniuk of the Ontario Cancer Foundation said: 'Doctors tend to undertreat in this country (the United States) because they fear complications will lead to a law suit. People are suing themselves into second class medicine by pursuing this mentality. They are binding their physician's hands'[5]. And indeed that is so true.

The American College of Surgeons is a very prestigious group of surgeons. In order to become a fellow, you have to pass your boards, and you have to demonstrate senior experience as a surgeon. That group did a survey of its membership and found 40 per cent of surgeons in the College were no longer accepting high-risk cases in consultation and 28 per cent were limiting the procedures they perform solely because of the threat of malpractice[6]. I was involved in that study, and I can tell you a very significant portion of that 40 per cent are in tertiary academic institutions. So I ask you, if the most skilled of our specialists are not treating the sickest of our patients, who is and at what cost?

Now I know you've had some professional liability problems here, and Sir George has talked about obstetrics. The American College of Obstetricians and Gynaecologists (ACOG) conducts on-going surveys of their membership because of the great concern over obstetric coverage in our country. Figure 3 shows the most recent survey done just this past year, and indicates that in our country 70.6 per cent of obstetricians have been sued at least once, and 25.5 per

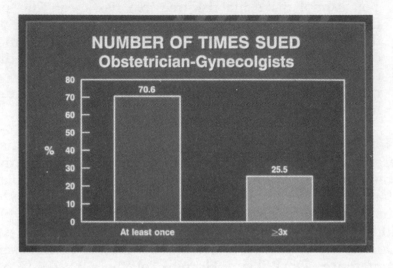

Figure 3

cent have been sued three or more times[7]. Think about that emotional trauma aspect. Think about the average verdict and you begin to see what we're doing to our obstetricians; what we're doing to all doctors. Let's look at obstetricians' professional liability premiums (figure 4). In 1982, the average obstetrician paid $10,946 per year, in 1990 that figure was over $38,000. In some of our busier areas such as New York and Brownwood County in Florida, an obstetrician pays $175,000 per year for a third of a million dollars in professional liability coverage before he opens his doors to practise.

Well what is that doing to obstetricians? They're retiring at an ever increasing rate at a younger age. In a prior survey in 1985, it was found that 26 per cent of obstetricians retired before age 45; in 1987 it's now over 50 per cent (figure 5). We have to remember that by the time an obstetrician in our system gets through medical school, post-graduate training, a year or two of Fellowship, he's in his mid 30s. So you can see many obstetricians are not spending very much time delivering babies during their professional careers. For

What may happen if there is no change in the UK system?

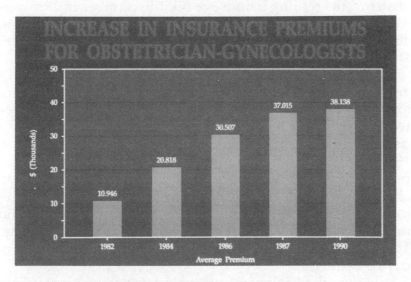

Figure 4

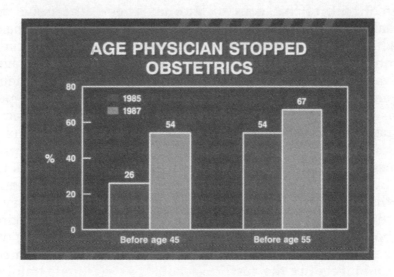

Figure 5

obstetricians retiring before age 55, the number in 1985 was 54 per cent and rose in 1987 to 67 per cent. When the current survey is completed, I'm sure the numbers will be higher still.

And there are other effects of professional liability that I am less comfortable about talking about in public. For example, the rate of caesarian sections. Around the free world it is clearly below 9 per cent, probably even below 6 per cent. In the United States, the rate of caesarian section in 1989 was 28.9 per cent, and that's simply because our system places the blame for every 'bad baby' in the lap of an obstetrician. And so the obstetrician is forced to go to caesarian section the minute there's any sign of trouble and much sooner than professional judgement would dictate. This is certainly having a very negative effect on the cost of our obstetric care.

And now the final area negatively affected by professional liability. We've talked about access to health care, quality of care and effect on physicians. However, the issue that gets the attention of people in Washington is the cost of health care. I've already indicated that we pay about $5.5 billion in the United States on professional liability premiums. I feel I must emphasise close to $4 billion goes to overheads and the great bulk of that goes to attorney's fees. The issue that really has people concerned is the cost of defensive médicine which is the type of medicine where you order every conceivable test, scan and X-ray so that an attorney looking through a 'retrospectoscope' cannot accuse you of negligence because you didn't order a single test. During the past six months I've been asked to Washington three times to speak to members of President Bush's Domestic Policy Council, to a senior administrative group from the Department of Health and Human Services, and to members of the Physician Payment Review Commission which, among other responsibilities, is charged with changing the way in which doctors are paid. What each group wanted to ask me about (I've been a great proponent of no-fault) was the cost of defensive medicine and if we had no-fault how much would it reduce the cost?

The costs of defensive medicine are difficult to quantify. It's been estimated everywhere in our country that it adds between 15 per cent of the cost of physician's services up to a third of the cost of health care. Through surveys at the American College of Surgeons, my own feeling is it's probably around 20 per cent of the cost of health care. Joseph Calafano, who was a previous Secretary of Health and Human Services and works with the Chrysler Corporation, thinks it's about 25 per cent, but it's a very significant number. Let me give you just one example of what defensive medicine is all about. We recently had a case at a Boston Hospital where in one of their out-patient facilities a patient came in who had slipped getting out of his truck and struck the back of his neck. The man had a completely negative neurological examination. The doctor treated him with just mild sedatives, some heat to the back of the neck, and told him to come back in three days if he wasn't feeling better. This man was a weight-lifter, went out and lifted weights, and three weeks later he came in because he was feeling numbness and tingling in his hands. He was immediately taken to have an X-ray of his neck which was negative, CATscan (computerised automated tomographic scan) of his neck was negative, and MRI (magnetic resonance imaging) which showed a herniation of a cervical disc. He was immediately taken to the OR (operating room) and the disc was removed. The man was left a quadriplegic. The judgement was $12 million against the emergency room physician. This was a patient who when initially seen had no signs, no neurological signs or symptoms yet the doctor was deemed negligent.

Now do you know what happens when a patient comes in to any emergency room complaining of even mild trauma to the neck or back, not only in New England, but probably throughout the United States? The first thing that happens is he gets an X-ray of his neck or his back; he gets a CATscan; he gets an MRI. The costs of these – I roughly estimate – are about $150 for an X-ray, $5–600 for a CATscan, $1–2,000 for an MRI. That's routine *modus operandi* now for emergency room doctors, and that's defensive medicine which is just runaway in our country. We have the technology, and we're just being forced (in my opinion) to overutilise it.

Again, President Bush at that same Commencement address speaking to the doctors there:

'I ask you today to avoid the understandable urge to practice "defensive medicine" where doctors fearing litigation too often dictate treatment that is unnecessary, where the threat of lawsuit threatens the very research that is so very desperately needed today to save lives. In return, we have got to restore common sense and fairness to the American malpractice system.'

Ok, where do we go from here? It seems to me there was a chap from these parts a few years ago who had the ideal solution, and I don't understand why it's taken so long to implement.

'The first thing we do, let's kill all the lawyers.' (William Shakespeare: *King Henry VI, Part II, iv*). How can we solve the liability problem? Very quickly. Arbitration – we have a number of states that have that option, but it is simply not used. Arbitrators tend to be very lenient and very generous. We have had one significant study done in the State of California which showed that arbitration cost no less than the current tort system and took only three months less than the traditional tort system[8].

Administrative alternatives, using mediators and the like have not proved very satisfactory. Contractual limitations on medical practice liability (things written into contracts when you buy your insurance) while they appear attractive, have been struck down on appeal by virtually all the superior courts. 'Early tender offer' is a system advocated by a law professor from Virginia, Jeffrey O'Connell, which would allow a physician who feels he has had a case of medical negligence to make an offer of settlement to a patient, and if that offer were accepted, the patient would be precluded from suing[9,10]. There are also several fault-based administrative models that have been proposed, and finally a patient compensation plan which is the so-called 'no-fault'. It's a solution for which I've had great enthusiasm for many years. It satisfies what I consider to be the absolute necessary components. We must have equality of remedies that is, like compensation for like injuries, and we must spread the cost over all at risk.

In the United States only 1:16 patients who has a medical maloccurrence ever receives any compensation[11]. Usually the persons who do receive it are given awards out of all proportion to their loss. And that just simply doesn't make sense. We want to spread the risk. We cannot have patient insurance as this is and expect less than 0.2 per cent of our population, mainly physicians, to pay for it. It has to be spread over all those at risk, and it will be indeed a very small cost. And finally, as has been brought out by this conference, and is so important to society, there has to be accountability and responsibility.

Our plan is patient insurance, and it would be voluntary. It would eliminate the need to prove negligence. It would establish an independent commission which would be appointed by the Governors of States, if it was done on that basis, or the President if it were done nationally. A significant number of its members would be insurance company people (because this is insurance) with a fairly large number of physicians, so that we could ensure accountability and peer review. Our plan would cover net economic loss only (no general damages), all out-of-pocket expenses, plus lost wages. Claims could be filed by patients who are much more sophisticated today. In the United States, I can think of at least 12 medical newsletters that are aimed at patients (that come from some of our prestigious universities) to help them gain some insight into medical illness, healthy living and preventive medicine. I would submit to you that our patients today do know when they have suffered a maloccurence. For example, Mrs Jones has gone in and had a gall bladder out and is discharged in two or three days. If Mrs Smith goes in and has a lot of problems and has to spend three weeks and has to be re-operated on, I would submit that she knows that things aren't right. We would also educate our patients along with providing this insurance. Claims could be filed by physicians and/or hospitals. A very strong medical professional review board would be established to review hospitals and physicians experiencing repeated claims. Costs would be spread over all those at risk – I've already mentioned that.

The advantage of our plan would be improved quality, access, cost of health care, and the elimination of the negative effects that are now occurring in our health care system. We would compensate far more patients in a fair, timely, efficient and affordable manner and we would identify sub-standard practice more efficiently. I think it's been well brought out earlier that bad cases are settled very quickly by insurance companies, but substandard practice is not easily identified. Sub-standard practice would be identified far more efficiently with our system because a significant number of additional cases would be identified and compensated.

One of the criticisms of a no-fault plan that I've had to deal with over the years is that it would be too costly. 'If you're going to cover all maloccurrences, you'd bankrupt any system'. We had an excellent study done by Harvard University, primarily Harvard Law School, Harvard School of Public Health with a small contribution from Harvard Medical School, just completed this past year in which 31,000 hospital cases were reviewed[12]. Using data from hospitals in the State of New York, they showed that a no-fault system would cost no more than our current fault-based system. If we could eliminate just a fraction of defensive medicine we could save very large sums of money. We spend $700 billion in the United States, just over 12 per cent of our GNP on health care. To save just a tiny fraction of the defensive medicine cost by implementing our no-fault plan would yield an enormous cost benefit result.

There's also been the concern that the current system deters professional liability. This has been alluded to for the reasons that were mentioned earlier. However it is simply not true. The Harvard study re-confirmed this and there was a mammoth study by the General Accounting Office in 1987, which also indicated that deterrence was not present in our current tort-based system[13].

Clearly the beneficiaries of the no-fault system would be patients. Patients in a far greater proportion would be compensated much more efficiently and in a more timely manner. If business and government could save a tiny portion of their health and accident premiums by reducing defensive medicine, it would be very significant. Certainly physicians who undergo now the tremendous emotional damage to their families and themselves in the current system would benefit. Who would suffer? A small number of malpractice attorneys.

At the present time, let me tell you what is happening in Massachusetts. We currently have a patient compensation Bill being heard before the Massachusetts legislature[14]. Last Tuesday I testified in favour of this 'no-fault' bill. The Massachusetts Bar Association dutifully came in and testified against it. Massachusetts physicians pay $160 million a year for malpractice insurance and over $100 million goes to attorneys. The Vice President of the Massachusetts Bar Association was asked how many people really specialise in this kind of work? And he said 'Well not too many, sir.' The Chairman of the Legislative Committee countered: 'Well give me a rough estimate.'.

He said: 'Up to 40'. Every year in Massachusetts malpractice attorneys receive over $100 million a year. A tremendous incentive to keep the system going. (The Bill is currently being heard before the Senate Ways and Means Committee).

Before I left Boston I was given the results of a study done by the American Law Institute[15]. The American Law Institute is one of the most prestigious legal organisations. It is composed of judges, law professors, etc. They have done an extensive study on enterprise responsibility for personal injury. I have a summary here – it's very long. To quote you from their summary:

'We are persuaded of two related judgements about no-fault liability accidents: first, the no-fault model should be considered a serious and plausible alternative in the ongoing debate about how best to deal with medical injuries. Second, medical no-fault can and should be introduced initially only on a voluntary elective basis.'

Which is precisely what we have always advocated.

So, in conclusion, professional liability is the number one problem facing physicians in the United States today. Repeated surveys by the American College of Surgeons, by the American Medical Association continue to put professional liability at or near the top of the list of issues adversely affecting the practice of medicine. Professional liability affects virtually everything we do from the patients we see in consultation and the diagnostic tests we order, to the treatments we perform. It just hangs over us like a dark cloud. It's there every time the patient goes into labour and the surgeon enters the operating room. It permeates every aspect of our professional behaviour. It is negatively affecting access, quality and cost of health care, and is literally terrorising our doctors. I have great hope and confidence that you will change the system here in the United Kingdom and not allow it to deteriorate as it has in the United States. Thank you.

References

1. *Edwards v Kuruvilla*. December 1988, Phoenix, Arizona.
2. Crane M. Will this case ignite another malpractice explosion? *Medical Economics*, Oradell N J, 1990; Nov 12: 42–46.
3. Charles S C. Malpractice suits: their effect on doctors, patients and families. *J Med Assoc Ga*, 76:171, 1987.
4. Rostow V P, Osterweis M, Bulger R J: Medical professional liability and the delivery of obstetrical care. *N Engl J Med* 1989; 321:1057–60.
5. American Cancer Society Annual Science Writers' Symposium, Daytona Beach, Fla, March 1986.
6. Professional liability survey report. Chicago: American College of Surgeons, 1984.
7. Professional liability and its effects: report of 1990 survey of ACOG's membership. Washington DC: American College of Obstetricians and Gynaecologists, September 1990.
8. Mills D H, Boyden J S & Rubsamen D S. Medical insurance feasibility study. California Medical Association and California Hospital Association, 1977.
9. O'Connell J: Offers that can't be refused: foreclosure of personal injury claims by defendant's prompt tender of claimant's net economic losses. *Northwestern Univ Law Review* 1982; 77:589–632.
10. O'Connell J: *Neo-no-fault: A fair-exchange proposal for tort reform in new directions in liability laws*. Walter Olson, ed. New York, The Academy of Political Science, 1988.
11. Harvard Medical Practice Study; Cambridge, MA, 1990.
12. Patients, doctors, and lawyers: medical injury, malpractice litigation, and patient compensation in New York. A report of the Harvard Medical Practice Study to the State of New York, 1990. Cambridge: *Harvard Medical Practice Study*, 1990.
13. Medical Malpractice: A Framework for Action. US General Accounting Office. Report to Congressional Requesters. GAO/HRD–87–73. Washington 1987.
14. The Commonwealth of Massachusetts House Bill H4217. 'An Act to Establish a System of Compensation for Injuries Related to Medical Treatment'.
15. The American Law Institute published a two-volume Reporter's Study on 'Enterprise Responsibility for Personal Injury' on 15 April 1991 (The American Law Institute, Philadelphia, PA). In their conclusion, they said the following:

What may happen if there is no change in the UK system?

'We are persuaded of two related judgments about no-fault liability accidents: first, the no-fault model should be considered a serious and plausible alternative in the ongoing debate about how best to deal with medical injuries. Second, medical no-fault can and should be introduced initially only on a voluntary elective basis...'.

Discussion

Chairman

Well, powerful stuff. The floor is open again for all of you. Who would like to go first?

Mr Mats Magnusson

Dr Manuel, now we have heard your version of the story, what do the lawyers say about these things? How are they – in short, defending the system that exists now in US?

Dr Barry Manuel

They work in a variety of ways. In terms of the testimony, they really don't do a very good job. What they do exceedingly well is dominate all our legislators and our legislatures. They have a significant representation in the State legislature, in the United States Congress. It makes it very difficult to get anything enacted which adversely affects the legal profession. They have claimed in the past that no-fault takes away patients' rights, but our plan is voluntary. When we point that out, their response has not been very scholarly. And I think the study I've just referred to by the American Law Institute is very important. These are some of the most prestigious legal minds in our country and they are now on record as favouring an effort at voluntary no-fault.

Mr David Bolt

I wonder, Mr Chairman, if I could just ask Dr Manuel a factual question which has always puzzled me? Clearly, as he referred in his remarks, the existence of the contingency brief in the United States is obviously an important factor in the level of litigation which goes on. Now is the implication of that, that in the United States you do not have the cost system that we have in the UK, whereby the unsuccessful party to a law suit pays the costs of the other side, because presumably the lawyers would not take on a contingency brief if they were going to pay the other side's costs if they lost it?

Dr Barry Manuel

We do not have that, at present, in any state. It was implemented in the State of Florida when the Florida Medical Association thought the system here was preferable and they spent enormous energies and resources to get that very law passed. Would you believe the very first case was a paediatric case treated in the emergency room, where (after going through the legal system) damages awarded to the plaintiff were in excess of $11 million, and in addition because of the new law there had to be a payment of $4 million to the plaintiff's attorney. That one case energised the Medical Association to say we have made a terrible mistake and the law was thereafter repealed following just one significant landmark case. So we now only have the contingency fee and our lawyers say that if you take away the contingency fee, you take away the poor person's right to justice. What they don't tell you is that most of our lawyers will admit to not handling cases that have a very small potential for fiscal remuneration. I have information here from Medicare which covers about 33 per cent of health care in the United States. Medicare recipients have about the same incidence of maloccurrences as in the non-Medicare population, yet their payment from professional liability insurance companies is only 5.3 per cent. It is far less because they don't have the potential for the large awards that younger patients have and the rest. It's not a very fair system.

110

Mr Brendan Phelan
Principal Officer, Department of Health, Dublin

Could I ask one question of the two speakers from the afternoon and one referring back to the morning? As I understand it, both in Ireland and in Britain, presently when a judge is attempting to set an award he cannot take into account any benefits which may actually flow from the NHS or from state provision, and certainly, in some of the more serious brain-damaged cases, a lot of these costs fall on the state, perhaps when the parents are no longer able to look after a brain-damaged individual. And perhaps the real cost of moving to a system based on meeting needs through the social security or a social welfare system are much less than they would appear to be. If perhaps this afternoon's speakers would comment on that?

And second, relating to this morning, I was impressed with the New Zealand example, in a small country of the effect of adverse publicity where everybody knows everybody else. Except that it may be even more the case where all doctors know one another, and how exactly can you get an effective and acceptable level of self-regulation in a relatively small medical community?

Sir Kenneth Keith

Well in terms of the first question, we do, of course, in a sense have an integrated scheme. If somebody is benefiting under the Accident Compensation Scheme, then that's the range of benefits which they are getting from the state. There is the occasional situation where the social welfare scheme might be slightly more generous, but they're pretty unusual, and in that case you may get the odd case of topping up by social welfare of accident compensation. But on the whole the Accident Compensation Scheme is complete and entire, and that's the essence of it. People might, of course, on top have private insurance in some situations which might give them additional income supplement, for instance.

On adverse publicity, Chris James really touched on that element earlier, I think. There is always the difficulty, isn't there, in terms of self-regulation in a small society that people do know one another or they were at school together or their parents were. And that can, of course, apply even when you have (so-called) lay members added to the process. But nevertheless I think we do have a growing sense in New Zealand that self-regulation with an increasing non-professional component (an increasing a lay component) can do a more robust job than it has in the past, and call people substantially to account. The professions themselves, not just the medical professions but others as well, are getting tougher about that as well, as failures of one kind or another are becoming more apparent and the need for greater discipline is becoming more apparent. And publicity is certainly a very large element in that.

Dr Barry Manuel

I would like to add the following comment. I think generally, your first point is very valid. Our society is paying for these people now, at least in the United States and we're doing it in a most inefficient way. We're spending 75 per cent of the money physicians pay to compensate medical injuries on administrative overheads and I don't think it's a very efficient way of dealing with it.

In terms of peer review, the Physician Mutual companies in the United States which cover 60 per cent of the physicians have only had to terminate the contracts of 0.6 per cent of their members for substandard practice. Now you talk about incentives; if you're paying for your colleague's mistakes, you suddenly find that a very, very expensive cost to friendship. And these Physician Mutuals have very strict peer review and it was revealed in a most recent study that only 0.6 per cent of physicians had professional liability insurance contracts terminated because of substandard practice. So I would submit that we do a pretty fair job of disciplining our own.

Mr Arnold Simanowitz
Executive Director, Action For Victims of Medical Accidents

Yes, at the risk of being accused of being discourteous to a guest from another country (Dr Barry Manuel) – and please don't take this as personal but I do think that was good, rough knockabout stuff, but I would ask the audience here (if they aren't aware that they should do so in any event) to regard what Dr Manuel said as totally and utterly irrelevant to this country. We are not going down that road. There is no way that we will go down that road. The system of delivering health care is different in that country. The whole ethic of America is totally different. I think it is unfortunate that we just have Dr Manuel here and nobody to represent the opposite view. Mr Mats Magnusson did ask him what the opponents say but you wouldn't expect Dr Manuel to put forward a very strong case, but certainly from what I've read about what other people say, it isn't exactly as Dr Manuel has put: that is the partisan view of a doctor under threat. And I think we must accept that.

Just to look at one example, he talked about the rate of caesareans going up. Now, I don't know what analysis has been done but we all know that physicians in America get a lot more money for doing a caesarean than for delivering babies in any other way. I mean this is the sort of thing that arises – I'm not an expert on the detail, but there is a very strong case (that is without seeing the case from the other side). But what we do know from this side is, for example, defensive medicine. All the studies about defensive medicine in this country have shown that it is not a problem. You've got Michael Jones, the law lecturer from Liverpool, who's done a lot of work on the subject and he has been able to demonstrate convincingly that it's not an issue[1]. At the King's Fund Centre, Chris Ham will tell you that when he did his investigation, defensive medicine was not a problem. The problems are not the same here. We have a different legal system. And as I say, the country is totally different. I mean when you look at a situation where a country won't even accept legislation to provide a seven-day moratorium for people who want to apply for a gun licence, you can see the difference between the situation there and the situation here.

Can I move on to some questions, one or two questions for Sir Kenneth Keith. What concerned me about what he was saying all the time and I think is inherent in the problems relating to the situation in New Zealand, is the inability to separate out the position regarding medical malpractice, or medical accident compensation and the rest. I was very surprised when he had to say this morning, when asked how many cases were rejected, that they don't separate out the two, and that four per cent were rejected. Well I should imagine that in relation to medical accidents the rejection is very much higher, and what I'd like to ask him is whether it isn't right that the whole system has been bedevilled by the fact that medical accidents really weren't understood, they were tacked on as an afterthought, they were personal injury therefore the system in New Zealand should deal with it? And all the problems that have flowed, all the issues, all the difficulties that he related, are difficulties which relate to the special nature of medical accidents. The system in New Zealand would have worked very much better if medical accidents had been dealt with in a different way.

And lastly, I think he's dealt with it, though I wasn't absolutely clear. I had information from someone on the Commission that in the recent review the thinking was to remove medical accidents from the system of no-fault compensation (the ACC in New Zealand) and I wonder whether he had covered that in suggesting that possibly it would move on to different phraseology; the question of injury, all injury or all illness? Or if not, what the other thinking is about dealing with medical accidents in a different way from ordinary personal injury accidents?

Sir Kenneth Keith

It's a little difficult to know about the final point in terms of the origins of the scheme. I don't think its fair to say that the whole system is bedevilled by the problems that arise in that particular area. The scheme as a whole operates in most of its parts without any real difficulty of the type that both Chris James and I were speaking about. Obviously there are problems that arise as we both discussed at the margin and they are problems that, in a way, are the subject of the second question. I don't know what would be the situation if they were to be dealt with in a different way. What does that mean? Because we are talking, after all, in terms of benefits – or in terms of entitlements – about the same things, that is: there should be appropriate medical benefits, rehabilitation and earnings related compensation, if that's relevant. And maybe, to go back to one of the proposals that has been made but not yet acted on, permanent disability

114

allowances for those who are very badly incapacitated. So I think the entitlements are likely to be the same, even if there were a separate scheme, and therefore its difficult to see why there should be a different scheme. I think the problems in terms of bedevilment, if that's the right word, are problems of definition and that does go to the second question.

So far as the question of inclusion or not is concerned the Law Commission in its examination of this matter didn't ever think of clawing back in that area and leaving medical misadventure uncovered. On the contrary, it thought that the movement should be in the opposite direction and the concrete proposal that it made was the one that I mentioned by reference to the WHO schedule which was an attempt to say, here is a statistical scheme, which has been developed by doctors around the world for identifying particular situations and which seems to give the ACC and the doctors (the people affected) a good practical way of identifying the areas which should come within the scheme and those which should fall outside it. Instead of this matter depending on the accident of decisions made by the ACC and by the tribunal and the courts in individual cases, we should try to get it right by way of a schedule which could be adjusted. So that's one way of trying to handle that medical problem, or the definitional problem.

The other way to handle it, of course, (as I indicated both this government and the previous government seem to accept it in principle subject to the money problems) would be to say let's cover incapacity by illness generally within the scheme, and then there would be no need to agonise over the definitional problems.

I take the first point that Mr Simanowitz made about the statistics. It is disappointing that we don't have some of these figures and I hope I'm not misrepresenting the ACC but as I mentioned some steps are being taken in that area to improve the statistics. It's been a recurring comment by the people who have looked at ACC from the outset that they have a marvellous opportunity to produce great statistics, dealing with a very large number of accidents in New Zealand, a very large number of injuries, and they haven't on the whole taken the opportunity. And that runs back, I think, to a problem with the perception of the scheme, indicated by the name. To talk about accident compensation is actually wrong. It's not about accidents, it's about incapacity or injury. And to talk about compensation, as Chris James mentioned, is to talk only about the third matter because what the Act says is that statute is about prevention and mitigation of injury in the first place. Second, it's about rehabilitation which isn't necessarily by money and lastly, in a sense, it's about giving people money to try to help deal with their problem.

Down the years, understandably I think, there's been a lot of attention given to that third thing and not enough to the very valuable information that's available to help with rehabilitation and to help with prevention and mitigation. Attention has tended to be too much at the compensation end and not enough at the research end.

Chairman

Arnold Simanowitz, you didn't ask Dr Manuel a question, but I think we should give him a right of reply.

Dr Barry Manuel

That's very kind. What I tried to do in my presentation is show you when we first began to notice professional liability in our country and how severe the situation is in our country today. I think the conclusions and extrapolations to the United Kingdom have to be your own.

Second, I think in terms of caesarian section, I am not expert on the remuneration of obstetricians in the United States, but you probably would be interested to note that an obstetrician is compensated exactly the same for a delivery, be it vaginal or caesarian, in Massachusetts. Finally I would say to you when I demean some of the responses of plaintiffs' attorneys it's because I can see no substance in them. I certainly agree I have come across as a proponent for no-fault and I acknowledge that. Nevertheless some of the best legal scholars in the United States have just come out advocating for a voluntary no-fault system. I have a great deal of confidence in their ability to look at our system and come up with an unbiased conclusion.

116

Mr Bertie Leigh
Solicitor, Hempsons

As a lawyer who works in England I'm bound to feel defensive of that status quo, and I still do though I must say after hearing Dr Manuel's caricature of – or a description of a caricature of – our system in America, I don't share Arnold Simanowitz's belief that these things can be treated benignly. It seemed to me to be a formidable attack and I would not like to defend their system. But as far as our system is concerned, I think it is important that we don't throw out the baby with the bath water and we do look very carefully at the virtues that we've got. People were talking about accountability in New Zealand, we have had a system of public accountability in the GMC for patients who wish to complain and have a public hearing of their complaints. We have sophisticated systems for private accountability to health authorities.

David Bolt was saying earlier this morning that he didn't think that the tort system had any component of accountability in it for the very good reason that indefensible claims would be settled very promptly and there wouldn't be a public hearing of them. I think the idea that health authorities are going to be content to dole out very large sums of money repeatedly and to close acute wards without taking any disciplinary sanctions against the clinicians responsible is distinctly optimistic and I should be surprised if there weren't a very sharp sort of clinical accountability developing in that fashion.

We also have the criminal law criticising doctors in this country where appropriate. I was slightly surprised by the cases which Chris James described. He described, for example, a wrong injection which led to a medical manslaughter prosecution of the physician. He didn't tell us what happened to the nurse who put the wrong ampoule in the wrong drawer, or handed the ampoule to the doctor without checking it herself. And I wonder if clinicians are properly protected in New Zealand or if there isn't some notion that clinicians are strictly liable for certain trains of events which isn't akin to our notion of the criminal law.

But if we come on to compensation, which is what we were talking about this afternoon, I find it very difficult to understand how when you're talking about which group of people should receive compensation, our guest from New Zealand could cite a scheme and repeatedly use the words 'fairness' and 'justice' in defence of it, when the author of it described it as illogical. What is a system for distributing compensation in a given set of circumstances? How can it be defended as fair or just, if it is illogical? For example, supposing I am admitted to hospital tomorrow and it's decided that I have a dangerous spinal or brain lesion. Now the surgeon may advise me to submit to surgery. He may advise me not to. He may or he may not mention all the risks which I should take into account. It may be that I will suffer a complete catastrophe because he wrongly advises me to undergo surgery or because he wrongly performs the surgery, or because he wrongly advises me against undergoing surgery. I'd like to know from Sir Kenneth, which of these categories would get compensation in New Zealand? And whether I would get the same compensation if I simply met with an overwhelming disaster because he decided that my lesion was inoperable and I suffered a catastrophe?

It seems to me that there is a certain logic in saying to somebody that if he causes profound damage, either he or the system which employs him, should compensate the victim of that damage. It seems to correspond to my notion of fairness and justice. To produce a statute which says that you can't have that compensation, you can have a pittance, which we all agree is inadequate compensation for that damage, and this will be spread amongst people who are not similarly the victims of a wrong; that doesn't seem to me to be fair at all. Where I did have some sympathy and where I was lured very much towards the New Zealand scheme was at the end when Sir Kenneth told us that it is proposed to extend the benefits of this system to all people who have suffered disability. That does seem to me to be fair and to be logical. It's very much what the Labour Party tried to introduce in 1945 when they came in and introduced a National Health Service. The idea that society could, as an item of policy, say that it will not provide proper care for people who need it when it is purporting to run a national health service, but it will provide the cost of care for people to purchase their care outside that system, that doesn't seem to me to be properly defensible at all.

If you were to say that you were going to introduce a proper system of health service for people to be maintained at the state's expense if they needed it and at the same time you were going to repeal another statute (which somewhat inexplicably the Labour Party also introduced in 1948) which says that in awarding compensation judges can't take any account of the likelihood that you will use the state system; that if you were to repeal, then you would bring levels of awards for brain-damaged cases very much more under control. And it would seem to me that that would be a pretty fair start towards our system. But I do not understand how one can simultaneously talk about fairness at the same time as taking away people's right, which the law offers them in this country: a right to get adequate compensation for a wrong which has been done to them.

It seemed to me that in Sweden we were told that you still have to prove fault and then you don't get proper compensation. And that in New Zealand you can't sue for proper compensation and you will get a level of award which has been limited to NZ$27,000 (£9,000) for a complete disaster. I would like to ask Sir Kenneth Keith when these monies were last increased and how many times have they been increased since they were introduced in 1974?

Sir Kenneth Keith

Could I go back to the fairness and justness and illogicality point? Yes, I'm sure I contradicted myself on that. The fairness and justice is, of course, as between those people who are incapacitated by injury. So far as they are concerned, since 1974, they have been treated on an equal footing. Their situation is one of inequality in terms of the incapacity they suffer. I quoted the passage from 1967 in which Sir Owen (Woodhouse) and his colleagues said 'In logic there is no answer', to putting to one side incapacity arising from sickness and disease. But the practicality provided the answer. Logic, on this occasion, must give way to other considerations. We should take two steps rather than taking a massive leap and we don't have the relevant information. And it was, of course, set up as a Royal Commission to look into people who were injured at work. Sir Owen was already drawing a fairly long bow when he

119

said that we should look at people injured at home or on the road, and so on, as well. So he was saying that there will be an anomaly at the border, there will be a problem. But he suggested taking one step this time, and hoping that another step could be taken later. And, as you indicated, that second step is under consideration now.

So far as the hypothetical that you mentioned is concerned, at least as I understood one version of it, in one of the various parts of the hypothesis it might still be possible to sue in New Zealand. It's not exactly clear where we are now following *Green v Matheson* in respect of an omission to treat or a decision not to take a medical intervention. On the literal approach, it could be said that in that case the doctor's action or non-action is not itself an accident which is causing an injury – there is no personal injury by accident. But there's some rather broad language in *Green v Matheson* which might suggest that situation is covered.

Now in terms of the argument that people should, if they have suffered profound damage, be able to seek payment from the people who caused the damage, well, sure, that's been the basis of tort liability for the last couple of hundred years though, you know, earlier than that there was a no-fault element sometimes, in some of those areas. But we have over a long time moved in a substantial way from that, in terms of no-fault schemes and workers' compensation and in terms of widescale insurance. And it's not, in fact, the person who causes the profound damage who pays but it is the wider community through whatever insurance or levy or whatever scheme it is.

In terms of the amounts of money, the comment was made that the amounts are inadequate and I think that's a fair comment in respect of the increase of the amounts that are payable for pain and suffering and loss of expectation of life and so on. Those amounts have been increased just once, to answer that question, about ten years ago, I think. About half way through the scheme they were increased. They haven't been increased since. They're plainly too low if they're to serve any real purpose but as I said, the argument that has been made for a good time is that they're inappropriate payments for a scheme which is supposed to be designed to rehabilitate and to get people back into the community. What has been proposed at various times instead of those lump sums, is that people who are seriously incapacitated permanently should be entitled to a continuing permanent pension which it was suggested could be worked out by reference to the American Medical Association Guides to the Evaluation of Permanent Impairment. There is a good deal of argument about at what threshold that would come in and how much the money would be. But I agree, those payments are inadequate.

In terms of the earnings-related compensation elements, you've already heard the figure a couple of times, of NZ$60,000 (£20,000) a year as the maximum amount which can be recovered for earnings-related compensation. And you might get that – thinking, say, of many people in this room – as highly-paid professionals, you might get that NZ$60,0000 a year for the next 30 years. Now that's a substantial amount of money. And you might in addition to that get very considerable rehabilitative help in terms of the reconstruction of your car or your house or whatever. So that at the top level some of the money that is paid out is substantial.

I should mention in that context, picking up the comments that have been made about how much of the money on other schemes doesn't go to the person damaged, that the administrative cost of the New Zealand scheme from year to year is usually well under ten per cent. So that 90 or 95 per cent of the money that is expended by the ACC each year actually gets into the hands of the people who are injured. On top of that the extra cost to the state of running courts and tribunals and the like is minuscule in the New Zealand case. As we indicated, some cases get to court but the amount of judge's time, the amount of courtroom time, the time of administrative support is minute under our system. So in that sense the money goes in the right direction, even if there's not enough of it, which is an ongoing argument.

Mrs Rita Lewis
Chairman, Association of Community Health Councils for England and Wales

We are a consumer body, an independent body, mainly of volunteer members with two staff. One of our main functions is to assist the public with complaints in the health service, and our remit is health service only. So that's the context from which I speak.

It's always very difficult when we compare other countries' systems with our own, and I'd like to focus onto our own now, because I think we've discussed a lot about other systems. The context clearly is different and the history is different in Sweden, New Zealand and United States to ours. I think also, importantly, the scale is very different. New Zealand appears to be similar in population to one of our regional health authorities, of which we have 14, so I think that brings it in slightly into perspective for us.

Over the years Community Health Councils (CHCs) have reported that the public are not happy with our complaints system in the health service. So we have currently reviewed that and we have produced a document which suggests a way forward for reviewing the complaints system as a whole. Within that there is dissatisfaction with this system of going to law to achieve compensation but the public do want compensation in certain circumstances, so I think that has to be one of the options to be considered. The problem with the law in this country is the limited access, the narrow perspective – it's just to prove negligence and the inequitable outcomes. You know someone might get a vast sum, as has been said here, for something that someone has to deal with because it was an injury or a disability they were born with and not as a result of accidents, and there's all sorts of things like that. There are also issues where people who are incapacitated are not included in this whole area. We've tended to talk about very articulate people who can voice their concerns, and know or can be advised what is wrong and what is not wrong. We wish to include the others, many people in the health service, for example, who are not capable of doing that.

So we would be looking more to a system of local independent reviews. A pro-active and re-active system, a system of constantly reviewing, in terms of medical standards, but also by peer group review with some lay representation. But also re-active where there are complaints to be looked at and people who will raise ongoing issues. In other words, we would be looking to a single-entry system where there are various levels of accountability, not just medical

122

accountability but various levels throughout the service and various remedies for that accountability when established. Compensation may be one of them, and then there would be the disciplinary action. So it would be one very unified, very simple system as we see it.

We have yet to work out how this would actually work, but that would be our view.

Chairman

There are several people wanting to get in and so if I can ask you to try and keep it short.

Mr Chris Hughes
Solicitor, British Medical Association

I think this final session has been something of a lovefest of the lawyers. However, in a back of an envelope calculation, I established that the legal costs borne in the USA applied pro rata would fund about 20 to 25 per cent of the New Zealand system of compensation.

Chairman

I wonder about the mathematics of that. Maurice Healy.

Mr Maurice Healy
Director, National Consumer Council

We supported Rosie Barnes's Bill, which was an attempt to bring in a no-fault system while retaining tort.

I'd like to come back quickly to the connection between compensation and accountability. It seems to me that compensation systems are, in the first place, addressed to an individual who has suffered something, and the characteristics of those systems are that, first of all, they should be user-friendly, accessible, should be quick and they should give people what they want. And what they want may be money, it may be a little bit of money or it may be a lot of money depending on their situation; or it may not be money, it may be simply access to medical care. It may be an apology. It may be simply to know what has gone on. And it's important in the judgement about all of that, that the judgement is seen to be fair and seen to be independent.

123

Systems of accountability are about more than the experience of a single individual, though obviously the single individual's experience is important. They are also about the experience of other people. They are about preventing further mistakes. They're about the general standards which are being held. Now, in those, the experience of individuals and their complaints is one thing, but I think it's totally inadequate to think of systems of accountability which are simply complaint-driven, and when the GMC, it is said, has a splendid system which deals with complaints; I simply don't think that's good enough. I mean one has to have systems which deal with incidence and not with complaints. We need to look at what is happening whether or not there is a specific negligent fault in legal terms. So I think that one needs systems – I mean such as the CHCs are thinking about, for some sort of inspection and some sort of monitoring as part of the accountability, and into that the experience of a compensation system is of relevant input. I mean the mistakes that somebody's made are clearly relevant but it doesn't seem to me that the system should in any way be restricted to that.

Chairman

Joe Smith.

Mr Joe Smith
Consultant Urologist, Radcliffe Infirmary Oxford

I suppose I now must regard myself as Treasurer of the oldest Physician Mutual in the world. I think that the MDU do pretty well, and always have done pretty well on the question of compensation. And I would strongly contest Mr Simanowitz's view that lawyers have done more for patients than doctors. The MDU compensates large numbers of patients who then obviously don't subsequently come along and complain to the AVMA.

I'm less happy about the way we deal with accountability, and I would like to know from Dr Manuel how the Physician Mutuals in the States deal with their members who have a less than satisfactory clinical performance? It's something we have great difficulty with.

Dr Barry Manuel

Physician Mutuals have a variety of mechanisms to deal with substandard performance. They can limit what physicians do. If they think they're not capable endoscopically, they can prohibit them from doing that. They can surcharge physicians who generate above average numbers of claims. They can impose significant deductibles. Finally, they can refuse to grant physician insurance. I will say in our country we do have a fairly stringent degree of scrutinising of our profession. We have to pass a three-day national examination to get licensed. Many states and specialty societies have mandatory continuing medical education requirements every year. Many have mandatory risk management requirements every year. We have board certification, which in our country is usually a two-day process, and now we have mandatory re-certification by many specialty boards.

Within the hospital model, we have peer review committees and quality assurance committees. We have federally supported and federally overseen professional review organisations (PROs) that are present in every hospital reviewing records of doctors, for any type of substandard practice or bad results. We are now beginning a programme of outcome assessments. Our federal government is estimated to spend over $100 million per year on this type of activity.

I would submit that the scrutiny of the profession is very comprehensive. In terms of your specific question, the Physician Mutuals do it by limiting privileges, using deductibles and/or surcharges, or refusing cover entirely.

Dr Roddy Quinn
Representative, Irish College of General Practitioners

I think one of the most impressive features of the New Zealand and the Swedish systems, which perhaps hasn't been alluded to enough, is the fact that there are hardly any complaints about the two systems. I think both speakers when asked, said that nobody would go back to the old system. There is actually nobody in favour of this. I would, however, fully accept the criticisms of the New Zealand system – or some of them anyway, alluded to by Mr Bertie Leigh. And I'm just wondering would Sir Kenneth Keith think in retrospect, as he is speaking from a country that has managed to take one step, would he advise those from countries who have managed to take no steps, that it would be in fact better to go for the leap rather than the two steps?

Sir Kenneth Keith

That's a very good question, if I may say so. I told an audience in, I think the southernmost medical school in the world, at the University of Otago, the other day the story, which many of you will have heard about Gertrude Stein's last words as she was being taken into the operating theatre for the last time – I don't think there was an action after this. She said 'What is the answer?'. There was a long silence. And then she said 'What is the question?'. And that was her last contribution. And it does seem to me that one of the really very difficult things, which is a matter that's got to be judged from one society to another, and one political system to another, is what is the question that is best addressed. Because after all the question that's being addressed today is just part of, isn't it, the question that was addressed in 1967 and 1974 in New Zealand, which was how should we rehabilitate and compensate those incapacitated by injury (see the 1967 Report). Obviously, the question then was why not all incapacity including incapacity by illness? Well that was not really within the brief of that Commission.

So I think it is a good question at any time. Whether it isn't better to go for a bigger step instead of simply medical misadventure. And various steps are being taken in relation to some of them, aren't they? As I recall it, the civil justice review gave rise to proposals for no-fault for some road traffic injuries, and I think that's been further considered. But I think that fragmented approach has its difficulties. It is a question for the wider political process whether it may not be better to say, let's try to have a wider approach to this and let's try, at least, to look at all injuries caused by accident, or conceivably, let's look at the really big question of all people who are incapacitated. But I haven't had the sense in talking to people in Britain over the last several years on these issues, that there is really a political willingness to take on those very big questions. The Pearson Commission, after all, tended in the end, didn't it, to approach the matter in a

126

fragmented way. But you never know. If you think of the way in which the world has changed in the last couple of years, especially this part of the world, maybe it is a time to be much bolder and to think of addressing the bigger questions, and then you will later have to deal within them, I suppose, with some problems that you might have over-looked by taking a very large leap.

I'm sorry it's not really an answer because I think the question has got to be addressed very much in your own political terms, but I think it is a good point often to say are we really looking at the right matter? Mightn't we re-focus this and look at a bigger question or, perhaps, a narrower one? And I think there's a lot to be said for, in this area anyway, for looking at really big ones and perhaps taking the leap.

Chairman

We're out of time, I think – David Bolt, you were indicating earlier, did you want to get in again?

Mr David Bolt

I only wanted, sir, not to leave unchallenged Mr Leigh's contention that the tort system was fairer than a no-fault compensation system. I won't hold up proceedings by going into it now, but I was just afraid that his undoubted forensic abilities might have unduly have persuaded the meeting.

Chairman

All right. Then I think that the moment has come, Dr John Wall, to ask you to speak last.

References

1. Jones M.A. & Morris A.E. Defensive Medicine: myths and facts. *J. Med Def Union* Summer 1989; 5:40–43.

Dr John A Wall

Summing up

Dr John A Wall
Secretary, The Medical Defence Union

On that last point, I agree with David Bolt. If I had just chipped in, not as a part of this summing up, I would have asked Bertie Leigh to agree that point was a personal one, though Hempsons, of course, are well-known to be the solicitors of whom the MDU is proud to be the client. It seems to me that the burden of today's discussion is that it is perfectly logical for a community (a question arises, how large a community can go down this logical track) to decide to keep its physicians, as part of the community, answerable to maintain decent standards by one means and to meet the common needs of people with similar disabilities by another means, namely financial. And I wouldn't want it to be thought that the MDU agreed with Mr Leigh's, what I have to say is his personal view, that there is no logic in a system whereby a community as a matter of maintaining peace and justice among its citizens, including its doctors, includes them in the community perhaps in the rather attractively austere way in Sweden, where it is perfectly clear to me from contacts over the past five years and from what's been said today, that doctors as part of the community accept that they are answerable to the community. They don't expect it to be a medical system which disciplines them. They perhaps have the advantage over the New Zealanders that they accept that there will be a community group which considers

129

whether they're maintaining good standards. And they accept that the community has its own logical and equitable ideas of how to meet the needs of those with disabilities.

Now, I wouldn't dream of summing up by repeating what's been said. That would be a non-starter. There have, of course, been some common threads during the day and I have the privilege of saying thank you to our speakers in a moment, but some points have cropped up which I think do need to be mentioned again. There's Barry Manuel who quoted Shakespeare, *Henry VI, part II*, 'The first thing we do, let's kill all the lawyers.' And Chris James quoted Samuel Pepys. Again, Sir Kenneth Keith has picked up the point which seems to me to be of crucial importance, the rapid change of public expectations, awareness, and the degree of being well-informed around the world in the last two years. Lech Walesa, President of Poland, was asked two years ago when the last of the Eastern European dominoes were falling: 'Could this all be reversed? Could the genie be put back in the bottle?'. 'No', he said. 'And it's because of mass communications. All the world knows what is possible. All the world wants what is possible.'

I've seen the film *The Verdict* with Paul Newman, in which as a trial lawyer, he achieves compensation in the courts in the United States – I forget which state, it may have been New York, it may have been Massachusetts – for the patient who was negligently treated in the operating theatre and then actively misled thereafter by the surgeon and his team, until Paul Newman found the nurse who was willing to disclose the truth and break the medical conspiracy of silence. I've seen that in the TV schedules in New Zealand, Israel and Wimbledon. It's a small world. All the world knows what is possible, and all the world wants what is possible. And it seems to me that those of us who have any influence should seek to steer it in the direction of what is equitable, possible and logical. It seems to me quite clear that there has to be a change from the present system.

I don't suggest killing all the lawyers. But it is quite clear to me that an awful lot of money goes to them as middle men and there is a major saving to be done. Sir Kenneth Keith has just made the point that the admirably small proportion which goes to lawyers of funds made available within the community to compensate those of us who have needs isn't more than ten per cent of the total. Anything which, as Diana Brahams has said many times in *The Lancet*, is half to the patient, half to the lawyers, needs something done about it.

What about the trust in the system of accountability? I have sons and daughters who've been undergraduates, including two or three at Manchester, where the students labour under a collective certainty that the police do not treat them equitably and any complaint is dealt with by the Police Complaints Authority. I won't labour the analogy except to say that from my experience, after 26 years at the MDU, and more particularly in the last three to five years, I go for the more austere, all-together community approach in Sweden. I prefer it to what Chris James has described where in New Zealand the doctors are finally trying to make their medically-controlled accountability system more acceptable to the public before, I suggest, the public insists on something controlled by the public. I think the GMC here should look very hard at the road down which the medical accountability system in New Zealand has gone. I don't think it's good enough, if the path chosen by Mr Nigel Spearing MP, simply enables the GMC to consider many more, and less serious, complaints. I think the public in Britain is insisting – and I don't think Mr Healy or Mr Simanowitz would disagree with me, that doctors are part of the community and cannot operate as if they were in some private bubble and would take in what information and give out what responses they choose, without being part of the community. That seems to me to be an insistence by the public to which the medical profession is going to have to concede.

The point was made, I think again by Mr Simanowitz, how will the patient know what has gone wrong? And I've heard it argued before that the solicitor has an ethical duty to disclose to his client when he has been negligent. And it's been said that the doctor does not have but should have the same duty. With all weight on that argument (and I give it the weight I think it deserves, which is considerable) is it not the case that recently medical claims have been conducted successfully and belatedly against health authorities by the second or sometimes the third firm of solicitors? And it's been made clear, however discreetly, that the first and the second firms of solicitors dealing with the case simply weren't up to the job. Now, they have never gone to their client and said 'We are conducting your case in a lamentable and negligent way', because frankly, they didn't have the insight. Now lawyers are human beings. I would like to submit that doctors too, are human beings. And that you cannot castigate a man who doesn't realise that he, doing his inadequate best, is not doing the patient justice in terms of what the medical community can deliver when performing competently. Now for that there are systems of accountability, of peer review – they're more complex in the United States – but here we've got excellent starts on internal audit within professions, within hospitals, within health authorities. I hope they won't be stifled by not having money added to them. I think of the health authority manager who brings in a monetary penalty element to the systems of quality review and quality assurance, to risk management, and with the help of his professional staff to audit. We need audit, all the better for it, about time the British hospital system had proper statistical audit of the outcome of types of treatment, of types of patients in types of suburb or central city, or rural district.

Alas, for the new NHS indemnity scheme. Sir Donald Acheson pointed out in his letter to Sir George Pinker that there was a danger – and again, the suggestion from our colleague from the Community Health Councils – that a single region may operate rather as New Zealand does. It is, of course, now the policy of the Department of Health that a region should operate more or less as if it were a country and without being too much influenced by what happens in the other regions. There is a peripheralisation as a political act of will at the moment. And there is a danger that the national statistics in Britain will not be gathered and will not be there from which to draw lessons with which to maintain high standards. Of course a defence organisation would deplore that, and we do.

As for the duty to disclose, I liked very much the contribution from my old friend, and contemporary as a medical student, Ian Field, the Secretary of the BMA, when he said we want to get away from the tort-based system which encourages concealment just at the very time when openness is called for. That is precisely putting the finger on the point. It is high time that any disincentive to frankness with

132

the patient in the present system were dealt with, root and branch, by changing the system. It's almost a good enough reason in isolation. Incidentally, with respect to the suggestion from Arnold (Simanowitz), we're not going down the same road as the Americans: in 1972 I was told by my then boss 'you are to write an article for *The Practitioner*, 2,000 words by tomorrow about litigation.' And I wrote that in the United States damages as high as £1 million were being awarded, and subscriptions as high as £1,000 a year were being charged to doctors. And in the case of the £1,000 subscription, I know about the loss of the value of money, but for the sake of illustration, we reached the £1,000 subscription in 13 years, and the £1 million award in 14 years. I've already suggested that the time-scale is shortening, perhaps from modern technology: the fast-forward button is on. As Lech Walesa says: 'With modern technology everybody knows things sooner and wants them sooner.'. I don't mean in a greedy, acquisitive way but in a matter of equality and equity between nations and communities. And I do think we're on the American road. And I think Barry Manuel has signposted it for us, and given the advocacy for the status quo from those who take more than half the total cash flow, namely the trial lawyers of America (I'm a subscriber to their journal). I think that Barry Manuel's advocacy was simply to restore a balance to the American picture which we need to look at frankly and thoughtfully, and decide how much further we wish to follow them down that road, given that we are now going faster down it than they were 15 years ago.

So there are the points. Affordability, of course. The suggestion was made that any system can only be to top-up the national insurance provision, whatever the country. Donald Harris, another New Zealander at Wolfson College at Oxford, has said many times that the best no-fault compensation system in the world is the British NHS. It's already been said by Mr Leigh. There, if you are injured or disabled, even through your own fault, perhaps drunken driving, lung cancer – arguably – is it your fault? I don't know, I don't smoke. Whatever happens to me will certainly be my fault. But the British welfare state will see that you don't starve, that you have a roof over your head, that your wife and children have a roof over their heads and they're fed and they're educated and your children are carried through to adulthood and self-sufficiency. Anything that tops that up is fine. Anything that gives what one of the lawyers at the Bar Conference, called a 'pools win' seems to me to be illogical and inequitable. And I think that's been the sense of what's been said today.

Now I'm not going to repeat what anybody has said. I don't think that's my place. I shouldn't do it. I can't resist the temptation to bring in Samuel Pepys. One more quotation. He wrote of the meeting in 1669 of what was the forerunner of the Royal Society established by Charles II: 'Dr Croome told me that at the meeting of the College tonight, which they have every Wednesday, there was a pretty experiment of the blood of a dog let out 'til he died into the body of another dog. The first dog died on the place. The other dog very well.'. The second dog had all his own blood let out and Pepys thought that if you let blood in one end and blood out the other, in a few minutes you've replaced the blood completely. Doctors know that isn't so. Harvey will tell us there would have been a mixing and there wasn't exactly 100 per cent change, but Pepys didn't know that. The first dog died. 'Other very well and likely do well. This did give occasion to many pretty wishes, as of a blood of a Quaker to be let into an Archbishop and suchlike. But, as Dr Croome says, may if it takes be of mighty use to man's health for the amending of bad blood by borrowing from a better body.'

And I thought of this which was in the notes I had with me, when I heard about the neonate given the single unit of blood for the amendment of his bad blood by borrowing from a better body. Now Samuel Pepys was the equivalent of the articulate media journalist with star quality. And yet, as Chris James quoted him, he was willing to say 'The Duke of Gloucester died of smallpox by the great negligence of his doctors.'. I am sorry to say that Pepys by 1675, if he'd gone on writing his diary then, if he'd had a competent oculist, might well have said 'They gave a pint of blood' (I won't imitate the language) From patient A to B. Patient B developed AIDS and it was clearly the great negligence of the doctors.'. The intelligent public wants doctors to experiment and to break new boundaries and it wants accountability. I suggest that the accountability should be as to reputation, intellectual probity, decency, but not money. I think how the needs of the community are met, it seems to me to be the consensus of today, and logically and deliberately be a different decision by the community. And I think the time has come.

I just want to finish by thanking the visitors today. It is an MDU exercise, as you can clearly see. I've taken the liberty of saying the MDU holds a certain view partly because by silence, the inference might be that we hold another. We are in favour of no-fault compensation and the separation of accountability from compensation. We thought that we would invite eminent practitioners of medicine and the law from other countries where they've faced the same dilemma we now face, and ask them to talk to us, as friends, at length, three or four of us might, in the next five years, have managed to meet all of them on various visits. The numbers of us who have faced the problem of making the health service in Britain, and the compensation system and the accountability system, work well in the 1990s as a matter of equity and fairness and logic, I suggest have benefited enormously by the trouble that our friends have taken to be here.

Dr Robert Maxwell in the Chair: the MDU has the good fortune that he is one of the advisers to the Council, to our great benefit, and we are grateful to you, Sir, for taking the chair today so effectively and gracefully.

Sir George Pinker, little needs to be said. He's an old friend first. Expert witness frequently. Ally. Setter of high standards, as we all know, in the obstetric community, and we're proud to have had you take part in our activities today, Sir.

Christopher James seems to me to be, from my old Roman history days at school, the Tribune of the People. Yes, he's the lawyer to the doctor who's under attack but his priority is the good of the people and the community in which he is a sterling upholder of the standards of legal practice, and it is an honour, Christopher, to have you here too.

Jan Sahlin, it wasn't at all evident that he was yesterday suffering terribly from a viral infection and couldn't eat and could hardly speak and was deathly pale. He looked a bit more austere yesterday than I intended to suggest when I said perhaps the Swedish system is austere. Two or three of us in the room have seen the compensation system in Sweden and we've heard it discussed. It's the first time I've had the pleasure or the privilege of hearing how the Swedish public community and the Swedish medical community mingle and do not keep themselves separate. I know from my own discussions with individual practitioners in Stockholm that they like being accountable to a group of their fellow citizens who don't have to be doctors in order to be entitled to ask them questions. I like the equality between doctors and the public in Sweden. I suggest that it may be the direction in which we should head in this country. It's not only that we are equal, we must appear to recognise that we are equal. So thank you, Jan, for coming and joining us today.

Sir Kenneth Keith was hospitable to Dr Alan Horler, the President of the MDU, and myself in New Zealand last year. I didn't dare to hope that we could somehow tempt him to spend some time with us in England this year. He knew immediately when we telephoned him before Christmas, what he would be doing on 13 May because it's his and his wife's wedding anniversary, and we particularly appreciate your making time for us today, of all days, Sir Kenneth. You're a lawgiver with your feet on the ground, if I may say so, and that is really a combination that we needed to have with us today, and we're very much in your debt.

As for Dr Manuel, I've already said that I think he's an advocate for balance where there is a very strong, I venture to suggest, more financial motivate than in the caesarian section point which, Sir, you so swiftly rebutted. I have the feeling that money talks in Massachusetts as it talks, of course, in Harley Street – as it talks in the Strand, I regret to say. And it's been a pleasure to me particularly, to hear the argument put so well that the legal system, aimed of course at equity, based on English common law, has perhaps gone off the rails – who can say – and is distorting the relationship between people and their doctors. If that's right, then you clearly need to do something about it. You've told us what's in hand. If you're doing something about it then it seems to me absolutely clear that we, too, need to. Again, Dr Manuel has made time in a very tight schedule. We heard some of the influential bodies which have asked for his advice on his side of the pond and we're very glad that he could make it here to join us today.

At this point I can stop summing up. I would like to thank also all of you good people who have your own active interests and strong opinions in some cases. We hope you will see that our aim has been to hear from the horses' mouths, what other people actually do to deal with accountability and compensation. How far, variably, they think the two should be kept separate. I have a feeling that, with the fast-forward button on now, the front bench of this particular Government really is playing King Canute. I'd like to think that they're the more sophisticated version, that know they can't keep the tide back but have to pretend, in order to impress their subjects.

At that I'll leave it. Can I thank all our speakers, all our visitors, all our participants, our staff, our hosts at the Royal College of Physicians. We are going to publish the proceedings. Part of the purpose of meeting today was to produce, not academic source material perhaps, except in some excellent examples, but something as a contribution to the debate which I'm convinced is necessary and I'm also convinced we'll see major changes in this country in the next five years. It is you, our visitors, and we hope to some extent, we of the MDU and our professional advisers, who have the task of steering what happens into a system which will produce fairness, equity, logic, justice and fair sharing of public funds to the people who need it with the minimum taken off in making it happen. Thank you very much.

Addendum

National Health Service (Compensation)

A
BILL

To provide that persons injured, distressed or subject to unnecessary pain or suffering during care by the National Health Service may be awarded compensation without having to prove negligence on the part of the National Health Service; to define eligibility for compensation; to establish a Medical Injury Compensation Board and to make other provision for the assessment of eligibility and payment of compensation; and for connected purposes.

Present by Mrs Rosie Barnes,
supported by
Mr Jack Ashley, Mr John Cartwright, Mr Tom Clarke,
Mr Frank Field, Ms Harriet Harman,
Mr Charles Kennedy, Mr Archy Kirkwood,
Sir Michael McNair-Wilson, Mr Alfred Morris,
Dr David Owen and Mrs Ann Winterton

Ordered, by The House of Commons,
to be Printed, 5th December 1990

LONDON: HMSO

Printed in the United Kingdom by HMSO

£3·10 net

[Bill 21]   (302117)   50/4

ISBN 0 10 302191 4

A

BILL

TO

A.D. 1991. Provide that persons injured, distressed or subjected to unnecessary pain or suffering during care by the National Health Service may be awarded compensation without having to prove negligence on the part of the National Health Service; to define eligibility for compensation; to establish a Medical Injury Compensation Board and to make other provision for the assessment of eligibility and payment of compensation; and for connected purposes.

BE IT ENACTED by the Queen's most Excellent Majesty, by and with the advice and consent of the Lords Spiritual and Temporal, and Commons, in this present Parliament assembled, and by the authority of the same, as follows:—

Purposes **1.** The purposes of this Act are: 5

    (a) to provide that compensation for injuries suffered due to mishaps during National Health Service care shall be available without proof of negligence;

    (b) to secure that National Health Service patients have the benefit of the same implied terms as to quality and description in 10 respect of goods (including medicines, blood and appliances) as private patients;

    (c) to seek to ensure that public monies available for caring for and compensating patients injured during National Health Service care are spent on those purposes; and 15

    (d) to minimise mishaps and compensation payments from public funds by enabling other action to be taken so as to maintain standards of care and management within the National Health Service.

Interpretation. 20

2.— (1) This section has effect for the interpretation of this Act.

(2) "The Board" means the Board established under section 3 below.

(3) "National Health Service care" means the provision of treatment,
1977 c. 49. services, goods and facilities to the public under the National Health
1978 c. 29. Service Act 1977, the National Health Service (Scotland) Act 1978 and 25
1990 c. 19. under Parts I and II of the National Health Service and Community Care Act 1990.

(4) "Mishap" includes, but is not restricted to, any act or omission which gives rise to an action at common law (or for breach of contract or statutory duty) by a patient in respect of National Health Service care. 30

140

(5) A person sufers "injury", where as a result of a mishap in National Health Service care and not as a foreseeable and reasonable result of that care or the person's pre-existing condition, he—

(a) dies; or

5 (b) requires in-patient hospital treatment for 10 or more days; or

(c) suffers significant pain, disability in normal activities for 28 or more days; or

(d) suffers significant pain, disability, harm, or distress or significant loss of amenity; or

10 (e) suffers a reduction in his life expectancy.

3.—(1) There shall be a body corporate to be known as the Medical Injury Compensation Board.

Medical Injury Compensation Board.

(2) The Board shall consist of a Chairman and not fewer than 14 nor more than 16 other members, appointed by the Secretary of State.

15 (3) The Chairman shall be a judge of the Supreme Court of England and Wales, appointed after consultation with the Lord Chancellor, or a judge of the Court of Session, appointed after consultation with the Lord Advocate.

(4) Of the other members of the Board, who shall be appointed after 20 consultation with such organisations as the Secretary of State considers appropriate,—

(a) 3 shall be medical practitioners;

(b) 3 shall be practising solicitors, barristers or advocates;

(c) 2 shall have experience of management within the National 25 Health Service;

(d) 2 shall be health care professionals (other than within (a) above); and

(e) not more than 6 nor fewer than 4 shall be persons other than those falling within (a) to (d) above.

30 (5) In appointing any member who falls within subsection (4)(e) above, the Secretary of State shall have regard to the desirability of appointing persons who have experience in, or knowledge of —

(a) the provision of health services;

(b) the provision of legal services;

35 (c) consumer affairs;

(d) social conditions;

(e) the maintenance of professional standards in professions other than the medical profession; or

(f) counselling or assisting patients who have suffered injury in 40 National Health Service care.

(6) The provisions of Schedule 1 shall have effect with respect to the constitution, procedure and powers of the Board and related matters.

Functions of the Board.

4.—(1) The Board shall establish and maintain a separate medical injury compensation fund, into which shall be paid any money paid by the Secretary of State under section 10(1)(a) below.

(2) In exercising its functions, the Board shall have regard to any code of guidance for the time being approved by the Secretary of State under section 8 below.

(3) On receiving a claim from —

(a) a person who has suffered injury; or, where that person has died or is a minor or is incapacitated, from his personal representative, guardian, or dependant; or

(b) a person acting on behalf of a person falling within paragraph (a) above,

the Board shall investigate the claim.

(4) A claim within subsection (3) is one which is made within 6 months of the claimant becoming aware of the injury and of its relationship with National Health Service care:

(5) Within 3 months of receiving the claim (or, where that is not practicable, at the earliest practicable opportunity), the Board shall notify the claimant of the results of its investigation.

(6) If the Board considers it appropriate it may offer and, subject to the other provisions of this Act, pay compensation to the claimant.

(7) An offer of compensation by the Board if not accepted by the claimant shall lapse 2 months after it is sent by post or otherwise notified to the claimant, unless the Board agrees to extend the offer in any particular case.

(8) Where the offer of compensation is accepted any legal claim the claimant may have in respect of the injury shall pass to the Board.

(9) Having regard to any code of guidance approved by the Secretary of State under section 8 below, the Board shall also take such other action in respect of a claim as it may consider appropriate.

(10) Schedule 2 to this Act shall have effect with respect to further, consequential and ancillary functions of the Board and the value of any legal claim that passes to it.

Availability of legal aid.
1988 c.34.

5.—Subject to the provision of regulations under the Legal Aid Act 1988, the making or refusal of an offer of compensation by the Board shall not prejudice any right which that person may have under the Act.

Relevance of public care provision.
1948 c.41.

6.—(1) In awarding the compensation in respect of any claim relating to National Health Service care, the Board and the courts shall apply section 2(4) of the Law Reform (Personal Injuries) Act 1948 (which provides that the availability of National Health Service care shall be ignored when awarding compensation for personal injuries) but with the words "regard to" substituted for the word "disregarded".

(2) Subsection (1) shall not apply in respect of claims brought by the Board or the Secretary of State against suppliers of goods to or for the National Health Service or any part of it.

142

7.—A patient supplied with goods in the course of National Health Service care shall have the benefit of the same implied terms as to description and quality and the same remedies as would apply where the same goods are supplied under a contract of sale within the Sale of
5   Goods Act 1979.

8.—(1) The Secretary of State may, after consulting such persons as he considers appropriate and after making any amendments he considers appropriate, by order—

> (a) approve any draft code of guidance prepared by the Board; or

10   (b) approve any modification of a code; or

> (c) withdraw his approval.

(2) The power to make an order under this section shall be exercisable by statutory instrument subject to annulment in pursuance of a resolution of either House of Parliament.

15   **9.**—(1) The Secretary of State may, after consulting the Board and such persons as he considers appropriate, make such regulations as appear to him necessary or desirable for giving effect to this Act or for preventing abuses of it.

(2) Regulations under subsection (1) above may also—

20

> (a) apply the provisions of this Act to prescribed descriptions of persons or in prescribed circumstances;

> (b) apply the provisions of this Act in such a way as to secure compliance with any obligation imposed by membership of the European Community;

25   (c) require prescribed persons to assist the Board in the exercise of its functions and impose financial penalties in the event of non-compliance with any such requirement.

(3) No regulations shall be made under this section unless a draft of them has been laid before and approved by resolution of each House of
30   Parliament.

10.—(1) *The Secretary of State shall pay to the Board out of money provided by Parliament—*

> (a) *subject to subsection (3) below, such sums as are required (after allowing for any payments which may be received by the Board in*
35   *consequence of section 4(8)) above to meet payments which are to be paid by the Board out of the medical injury compensation fund;*

> (b) *such sums as he may, with the approval of the Treasury, determine are required for other expenditure of the Board.*

(2) The Secretary of State may, with the approval of the Treasury,—

40   (a) determine the manner in which and times at which the sums referred to in subsection (1) above shall be paid to the Board; and

> (b) impose conditions on the payment of those sums.

(3) In assessing the sum of money to be paid under subsection (1)(a) above to the Board in its first year of operation, the Secretary of State shall have regard to—

    (a) the amount of public money expended in the previous financial year on administering, litigating and compensating claims in respect of National Health Service care; and   5

    (b) such other sums as he may, with the approval of the Treasury, consider necessary and desirable for the purposes of this Act.

(4) *There shall be paid out of money provided by Parliament—*

    (a) any expenses of the Secretary of State under this Act; and   10

    (b) any increase attributable to this Act in the sums payable out of such moneys under any other Act.

Extension of provisions to Northern Ireland.

11. Not later than the end of the period of six months beginning with the day on which this Act is passed, the Secretary of State shall lay before each House of Parliament a draft Order in Council extending the   15 provisions of this Act to Northern Ireland.

Short title and commencement.

12.—(1) This Act may be cited as the National Health Service (Compensation) Act 1991.

(2) Subject to subsection (3) below, this Act shall come into force on such day as the Secretary of State may by order appoint, and different   20 days may be appointed for different provisions.

(3) An order under subsection (2) may contain such transitional and saving provisions as appear to the Secretary of State to be necessary or expedient.

(4) Section 6 shall not be brought into force before section 4.   25

(5) Any power to make an order under this section shall be exercisable by statutory instrument subject to annulment in pursuance of a resolution of either House of Parliament.

SCHEDULES

SCHEDULE 1

THE MEDICAL INJURY COMPENSATION BOARD

Appointments

5   **1.**—(1) Every member of the Board—

    (a) shall be appointed for such term, not exceeding five years, as the Secretary of State may specify; and

    (b) shall hold and vacate office in accordance with the terms of his appointment.

10   (2) Any person who ceases to be a member of the Board shall be eligible for re-appointment.

    (3) A member of the Board may at any time resign his office by giving notice in writing to the Secretary of State.

    (4) The Secretary of State may remove a member of the Board if 15 satisfied—

    (a) that he has been absent from meetings of the Board for a period of more than six consecutive months without the permission of the Board;

    (b) that a bankruptcy order has been made against him or that his 20 estate has been sequestrated or that he has made a composition or arrangement with, or granted a trust deed for, his creditors; or

    (c) that he is otherwise unable or unfit to discharge the functions of a member of the Board.

25   *Proceedings of the Board*

2. The Board may regulate its own procedure.

Delegation of powers

    3.—(1) Anything authorised or required by or under any enactment to be done by the Board may be done—

30   (a) by any member of the Board, or of its staff, who has been authorised for the purpose, whether generally or specifically, by the Board; or

    (b) by any committee or sub-committee of the Board which has been so authorised.

35   (2) Any committee or sub-committee of the Board—

    (a) may include, as non-voting members, persons who are not members of the Board but who are co-opted by the Board;

    (b) shall be chaired by the Chairman of the Board or by another member of the board nominated by him.

145

(3) The Chairman of the Board shall be a member of any committee or sub-committee for which he has nominated another member of the Board to be its chairman.

Vacancies and defective appointments

4. The validity of any proceedings of the Board shall not be affected by a vacancy amongst the members or by any defect in the appointment of a member.

5. The application of the seal of the Board shall be authenticated by the signature of—

    (a) the Chairman or any other member of the Board; and

    (b) a member of the Board's staff who has been authorised by the Board for the purpose, whether generally or specifically.

Documents served etc. by the Board

6.— (1) Any document which the Board is authorised or required by or under any enactment to serve, make or issue may be signed on behalf of the Board by any person who has been authorised for the purpose, whether generally or specifically, by the Board.

(2) Every document purporting to be an instrument made or issued by or on behalf of the Board and—

    (a) to be duly executed under the seal of the Board; or

    (b) to be signed or executed by a person authorised by the Board for the purpose,

shall be received in evidence and treated, with further proof, as being so made or issued unless the contrary is proved.

Remuneration and pensions etc.

7.— (1) The Board shall pay—

    (a) to its members; and

    (b) to other persons who are co-opted to serve as members of any of its committees or sub-committees,

such remuneration, and such travelling and other allowances, as may be determined by the Secretary of State.

(2) The Board shall, if so required by the Secretary of State—

    (a) pay such pension, allowances or gratuities to or in respect of a person who has been, or is, a member of the Board; or

    (b) make such payments towards provision for the payment of a pension, allowances or gratuities to or in respect of such a person

as may be determined by the Secretary of State.

(3) If, when any member of the Board ceases to hold office, the Secretary of State determines that there are special circumstances which make it right that that member should receive compensation, the Board

shall pay to him a sum by way of compensation of such amount as may be so determined.

(4) The approval of the Treasury shall be required for the making of a determination under this paragraph.

5 *Staff*

8.— (1) The Board may, with the approval of the Secretary of State as to terms and conditions of service, appoint such staff as it may determine.

10 (2) The Board shall appoint at least one claims officer with respect to each Regional Health Authority or at such lower level of the National Health Service structure as it may consider appropriate.

(3) The Board, with the approval of the Secretary of State, may—

(a) pay such pensions, allowances or gratuities to or in respect of any persons who have been or are members of its staff as it may
15 determine;

(b) make such payments as it may so determine towards provision for the payment of pensions, allowances or gratuities to or in respect of any such persons;

(c) provide and maintain such schemes as it may so determine
20 (whether contributory or not) for the payment of pensions, allowances or gratuities to or in respect of any such persons;

(d) make such other arrangements for the provision of pensions, allowances or gratuities to or in respect of any such persons as it may so determine.

25 (4) Any reference in sub-paragraph (2) to pensions, allowances or gratuities to or in respect of any such persons as are mentioned in that sub-paragraph includes a reference to pensions, allowances or gratuities by way of compensation to or in respect of any of the Board's staff who suffer loss of employment or loss or diminution of emoluments.

30 (5) If any person—
(a) on ceasing to be a member of the Board's staff becomes a member of the Board; and

(b) was by virtue of his being a member of the Board's staff a participant in any pension scheme maintained by or on behalf
35 of the Board for the benefit of any of its staff,

the Board may, with the approval of the Secretary of State, make provision for him to continue to participate in that scheme, on such terms and conditions as it may with the consent of the Secretary of State determine, as if his service as a member were service as a member of the
40 Board's staff; and any such provision shall be without prejudice to paragraph 7.

(6) The consent of the Treasury shall be required for giving of any approval under this paragraph.

Accounts and audits

9.— (1) The Board shall keep accounts and shall prepare a statement
of accounts (the "statement") in respect of each financial year.

(2) The accounts shall be kept, and the statement shall be prepared,
in such form as the Secretary of State may, with the approval of the   5
Treasury, direct.

(3) The accounts shall be audited by persons to be appointed in
respect of each financial year by the Secretary of State in accordance
with a scheme of audit approved by him.

(4) The auditors shall be furnished by the Board with copies of the   10
statement and shall prepare a report to the Secretary of State on the
accounts and statement.

(5) No person shall be qualified to be appointed as auditor under this
paragraph unless he is—

(a) a member of a body of accountants established in the United   15
Kingdom and for the time being recognised for the purposes of
section 389(1)(a) of the Companies Act 1985;

(b) authorised by the Secretary of State under section 389(1)(b) of
that Act to be appointed an auditor of a company; or

(c) a member of the Chartered Institute of Public Finance and   20
Accountancy.

1985 c.6.

(6) A firm may be appointed as auditor under this paragraph if each
of its members is qualified to be so appointed.

(7) On completion of the audit of the accounts, the auditors shall
send to the Secretary of State a copy of the statement and of their   25
report.

(8) The Secretary of State shall send a copy of the statement and of
the report to the Comptroller and Auditor General.

(9) The Secretary of State and the Comptroller and Auditor General
may inspect the Board's accounts and any records relating to them.   30

(10) The Secretary of State shall lay before each House of Parliament
a copy of every statement and report sent to him under this paragraph.

(11) In this paragraph "financial year" means—

(a) the period beginning with the day on which the Board is
established and ending with the following 31st March; and   35

(b) each subsequent period of twelve months ending with 31st
March.

Monies and Investments

10.— (1) *The Secretary of State may, with the approval of the Treasury,
make to the Board out of money provided by Parliament grants of such*   40
amounts as he thinks fit.

(2) The payment by the Secretary of State of a grant under this
paragraph shall be on such terms as he may, with the approval of the
Treasury, provide.

(3) The Board may accept gifts.

(4) The Board may borrow money and invest money with the approval of the Secretary of State and subject to such conditions as he may require.

Reports of Board

11.— (1) The Board shall submit to the Secretary of State an annual report on the discharge of its functions.

(2) The Secretary of State shall lay before each House of Parliament, and cause to be published, the annual report of the Board.

(3) The Board may make to the Secretary of State, and publish, such other reports as it may see fit.

Immunity for advice and reports

12. For the purposes of the law of defamation, the publication of any advice or report by the Board in the exercise of any of its functions shall be absolutely privileged.

National Database

13.— (1) The Board may, with the approval of the Secretary of State, establish or participate in the establishment of a National Database, or such related scheme as he may approve.

(2) A National Database within subparagraph (1) above is one which maintains and collates data on cases involving medical mishaps.

(3) The Board shall make the data available for research and scientific analysis on such terms as it sees fit.

Appeals procedure

14.— (1) Where a claimant is aggrieved by the outcome of the investigation or any offer of compensation or both, he may apply to the Board for the claim to be considered after a hearing.

(2) A claimant may not make an application under this paragraph if, as part of its determination, the Board has certified that in its opinion no prima facie case for an award of compensation or other action was disclosed by his application.

(3) An application under this paragraph —

    (a) shall be entertained by the Board if it is made before the expiry of the period of three months beginning with the date on which the claimant was notified of its determination; and

    (b) may be entertained by the Board if made outside that period if it is satisfied that there are exceptional reasons for doing so.

(4) The Board may refuse an application under this paragraph if it is of the opinion that there is sufficient reason to do so and, if the claimant so requires, shall give him a certificate that the application has been refused.

149

SCH. 1   (5) Where the Board refuses an application for the reconsideration of a claim determined without a hearing in accordance with the law of England and Wales, the High Court, on the application of the claimant, may make an order of mandamus requiring the Board to reconsider his claim after a hearing.   5

Legal proceedings

15.— (1) Where the Board elects to pursue a legal claim that has passed to it, it may instruct such solicitors and counsel as it sees fit.

(2) The normal rules as to costs shall apply to cases to which the Board is party.   10

(3) Where the Board pursues a legal claim that has passed to it, it shall do so in its own name and it may in any one proceeding seek compensation in respect of more than one mishap or claimants.

Training and research

16.—(1) The Board or its staff may conduct, attend, organise or   15 participate in any training sessions with respect to its functions or the purposes of this Act as it sees fit.

(2) The Board may arrange, conduct, inititate or participate in such research projects as it sees fit.

Parliamentary Disqualification etc.   20

1975. c.24.   **17.** In Part II of Schedule 1 to the House of Commons Disqualification Act 1975 (bodies of which all members are disqualified) the following entry shall be inserted at the appropriate place—

"The Medical Injury Compensation Board".   25

Sections 4 and 8.

SCHEDULE 2

OTHER FUNCTIONS OF THE BOARD: GUIDANCE

Introduction

1988. c.33.   **1.** In preparing any draft code of guidance under this Schedule, the Board shall have regard to any relevant provisions relating to the   30 Criminal Injuries Compensation Board in Schedule 7 to the Criminal Justice Act 1988 and to any rules made under that Schedule.

PART I

Guidance on claims (compensation)

2. Having regard to the definition of mishap in section 2, the Board   35 shall prepare a draft code of guidance for the purposes of section 8 on the further criteria by which it will determine whether a mishap has occurred during National Health Service care.

3. The Board shall also prepare a draft code of guidance for the purposes of section 8 on: 40

    (a) eligibility for compensation;

(b) the criteria for calculating offers of compensation;

(c) any limitations to items of compensation, including for loss of earnings;

(d) the relationship the claimant should establish between the injury and the mishap (having regard to the difficulties in establishing causation in law in such claims);

(e) the way in which compensation may be paid (including whether by lump sum, periodic payment or otherwise);

(f) the conditions to which an offer or award of compensation may be subject (including assisting in any other action within Part II of this Schedule);

(g) any reduction in compensation on account of the acts or omissions of the patient or the claimant;

(h) the extent to and circumstances in which provisional awards of compensation may be made and the procedure for subsequent reappraisal of a claim;

and such a draft code under this Part may make different provision for different descriptions of persons and for different circumstances.

PART II

Guidance on other action

4. Having regard to this Act and to the fact that—

(a) defensive medicine; and

(b) carelessness and the failure to maintain proper managerial and professional standards are not in the interests of the providers or consumers of National Health Service care; and

(c) the confidence of the providers and consumers of National Health Service care in the Board; and

(d) the prudent use of public money

are desirable the Board shall prepare a draft code of guidance for the purposes of section 8 on the criteria by which it will decide whether any course of action by it (other than an offer of compensation under section 4) is appropriate in respect of claims of any type.

5. The courses of action the draft code should cover include, but are not restricted to,—

(a) taking no action; or

(b) one or more of the following—
(i) obtaining an explanation, or seeking an apology for the benefit of the claimant, or both;
(ii) raising or following up any concerns with any person, or both;

(c) referring the matter to any appropriate authority or disciplinary body

(d) publicising the matter in its annual report or as it sees fit (having regard to representations about confidentiality);

(e) pursuing any legal claim which has passed to the Board (whether that claim is against the National Health Service or any part of it, or against a supplier to or for the National Health Service or to or for any part of it)

and such a draft code of guidance under this Part may make different provision for different descriptions of persons and for different circumstances. 5

6. Where the Board pursues any legal claim which has passed to it, the value of that claim shall not be restricted to the level of compensation that the Board has paid to the claimant, but shall be assessed by reference to the damages that would have been awarded to the claimant had he pursued the legal claim himself. 10

Part III

Investigations and publicity

7. The Board shall prepare a draft code of guidance for the purposes of section 8 on 15

(a) the way in which the Board shall investigate any claim;

(b) the evidence it may require;

(c) the use it may make of appropriate expert evidence;

(d) the extent to and circumstances in which evidence it has obtained shall be made available to the claimant or for other purposes, including any action under Part II above. 20

8. The Board shall also prepare a draft code of guidance for the purposes of section 8 on how it and its services may best be publicised and this may include— 25

(a) seeking to ensure that potential and prospective claimants are notified about the Board;

(b) publicity in the media;

(c) the distribution of relevant material through the National Health Service, government departments, the Post Office and voluntary agencies. 30

9. A draft code under this Part may make different provision for different descriptions of persons and for different circumstances.

Part IV

Other Guidance 35

10. The Board shall also prepare such other draft codes of guidance for the purposes of section 8 as it considers appropriate for the proper discharge of its functions.

11. A draft code under this Part may make different provision for different descriptions of persons and for different circumstances. 40